Wrexham Hospitals

a pictorial record

Wrexham Hospitals

a pictorial record

Joan Chaloner

First published in Wales in 2005
by

BRIDGE BOOKS
61 Park Avenue
Wrexham
LL12 7AW
Wales, UK

ISBN 1-84494-022-5

A CIP entry for this book is available from the British Library

Printed and bound by
CPOD a division of Cromwell Press Group
Trowbridge
Wiltshire

CONTENTS

Acknowledgements

I would like to express my sincere thanks to the following individuals and organisations for their help and guidance:

Mr Dylan Hughes (chief libraries officer, Wrexham)
Mr Andy Scotson (Yspyty Maelor Hospital Trust Board)
Ms Diane Henderson (Yspyty Maelor Hospital, Quality Control Department)
Mr John Thomas (reference librarian)
Dr E. G. G. Roberts (consultant paediatrician)
Mr David Barry Beckweth Whitehouse (consultant obstetrician and Gynaecologist)
Dr Pat Salt (GP and medical officer) Chirk Hospital.
Mr Orr (retired chairman of the Llangollen Cottage Hospital Management Committee)
Mr Wyndham Evans (former hospital secretary, Maelor General Hospital)
Dr Graham Arthurs (consultant anaesthetist/Nightingale House)
Dr Peter Hughes (archivist, Nazareth House, London)
Dr Ralph Whiting (retired consultant anaesthetist)
Dr John Marchant (retired consultant anaesthetist)
Dr Baker (retired consultant physician)
Mr Dave Thomas (environmental health depratment, Wrexham)
Mr David Castledine (Denbighshire Records Office, Ruthin)
Wrexham Social Services Department
Miss Mary Tagg (retired district nursing officer)
Miss Joan Gilbert (retired director of community services)
Miss Mary Sexton (retired director of midwifery services)
Mrs Myfanwy Povey (retired senior midwifery tutor)
Dr Malcolm Godwin (deputy head, University of Wales School of Nursing, Wrexham)
Mrs Ann Jones (administrator Wrexham School of Nursing)
Miss Doreen Pritchard (retired SEN tutor, Maelor Hospital)
Miss Gwyneth Roberts (retired SEN tutor, Maelor Hospital)
Mrs Eileen Walker (retired senior tutor, Wrexham School of Nursing)
Mrs Chris Morris (retired senior tutor, Wrexham School of Nursing)
Mrs Margaret Arkinstall (retired Hospital Community Liaison Officer)
Mrs Shirley Davies (retired matron, Llangollen and Chirk Cottage Hospitals)
Mrs Pat Kendrick (retired district nurse/midwife)
Mrs Dawn Cooper (head of Midwifery and Women's Services)
Miss Marian Williams (retired Senior Midwife, Maelor Hospital Special Care Baby Unit)
Bronwen Edwards. (retired S.E.N. Maelor Hospital Special Care Baby Unit)
Senior Sister Geraldine Gilbert (paediatrics department, Ysbyty Maelor)
Sister Oliver (Nazareth House, Wrexham)
Sister Gertrude (Nazareth House, Wrexham)
Mrs Mair Hughes (district liaison officer, Marie Curie Foundation)
Senior Macmillan Nurse Jackie Evans
Mr Eldred Ankers (retired chief technician pathology department, Maelor General Hospital)
Mr Eddie Bowen (solicitor, Ruabon)
Mr Gareth Davies (senior laboratory technician)
Staff Midwife Lucy Davies
Mr Ken Jones (historian of Penley Hospital)
Mrs Jean Roberts (retired staff nurse, Penley Hospital)
Mrs Nora Crump (retired District Midwife)
Miss Joan Britton (retired Community Midwife)
Mrs Enid Jones (retired midwife, Ruabon Hospital)
Mrs Shirley Randles (retired school teacher)
Miss Margaret Ingram (retired school teacher)
Mrs Olive Burns (retired school teacher)
Mr Ray Burns (retired Royal Marines)

Miss Martha Roberts (retired school teacher, British Red Cross Society)
Mrs Mary Edwards (retired nurse manager, Maelor Hospital)
Mrs Dinah Hughes (Broughton)
Mrs Gwyneth Haylock (health studies librarian, Univeristy of Wales, Bangor)
Mr Richard Bailey (John Spalding Library, Wrexham)
Mrs Jane Baker (John Spalding Library, Wrexham)
Mrs Phylis Edwards (retired midwifery sister)
Senior Nurse Mrs Williams (Trevalyn Hospital)
Mrs Eirlas Perrin (retired school nurse)
Mr Ray Davies (Mold)
Mr Gwyn Jones Davies (ex-Maelor Hospital)
Mrs Len Jones Davies (ex-Maelor Hospital)
Mrs Ada Roberts (retired sister, War Memorial Hospital)
Mrs betty ap Thomas (retired sister, War Memorial Hospital)
Mr John Garsden and Collette and Sharon (manager and staff, HSDU)
Mrs Gwyneth Grant (retired SEN, Croesnewydd Hospital)
Ms Mary Giller Williams (retired SEN, Maelor Hospital)
Mrs Gwen Cuthbert (St John's Ambulance, Wrexham)
Mr Harry Downs (St John's Ambulance, Wrexham)
Mr Reg Williams (St John's Ambulance, Wrexham)
Mr David Basil Cole (L. Rowland and Co)
Mr Peter Wilson (retired charge nurse, Llangwyfan Hospital)
Mr Brian Colishaw (retired lab technician, Llangwyfan Hospital)
Mrs Myra Jones (retired, SCBU)
Mr Alf Jones (retired, ECG Department)
Mrs Nell Jones (retired sister War Memorial Hospital)
Mrs Ivy Roberts (retired SEN Isolation Hospital and Maternity Unit)
Mrs Margaret Jones (retired domestic services supervisor, Maelor General Hospital)
Mr Tom Jones (retired porter Maelor General Hospital)
Mrs Josephine Smullen (retired sister, Maelor General Hospital)
Ms Heulwen Roberts (retired midwifery sister, Maelor General Hospital)
Ms Rhona Jones (staff midwife)
Mrs M Edwards (retired nurse manager, Maelor General Hospital)
Mr Charles Cathrall
Miss Joy Thomas (A N Palmer Centre, Wrexham)
Mr Neville Hurdsman (local historian, author of *History of Chirk*)
Mr Graham Rogers (local history author)
Mr Tom Evans (local historian)
Wrexham Evening Leader

Joan Chaloner

Abbreviations for picture captions:

WMS	Wrexham Museum Service
WAWC	W Alister Williams Collection
DRO	Denbighshire Record Office, Ruthin

Pedigree of Ysbyty Maelor

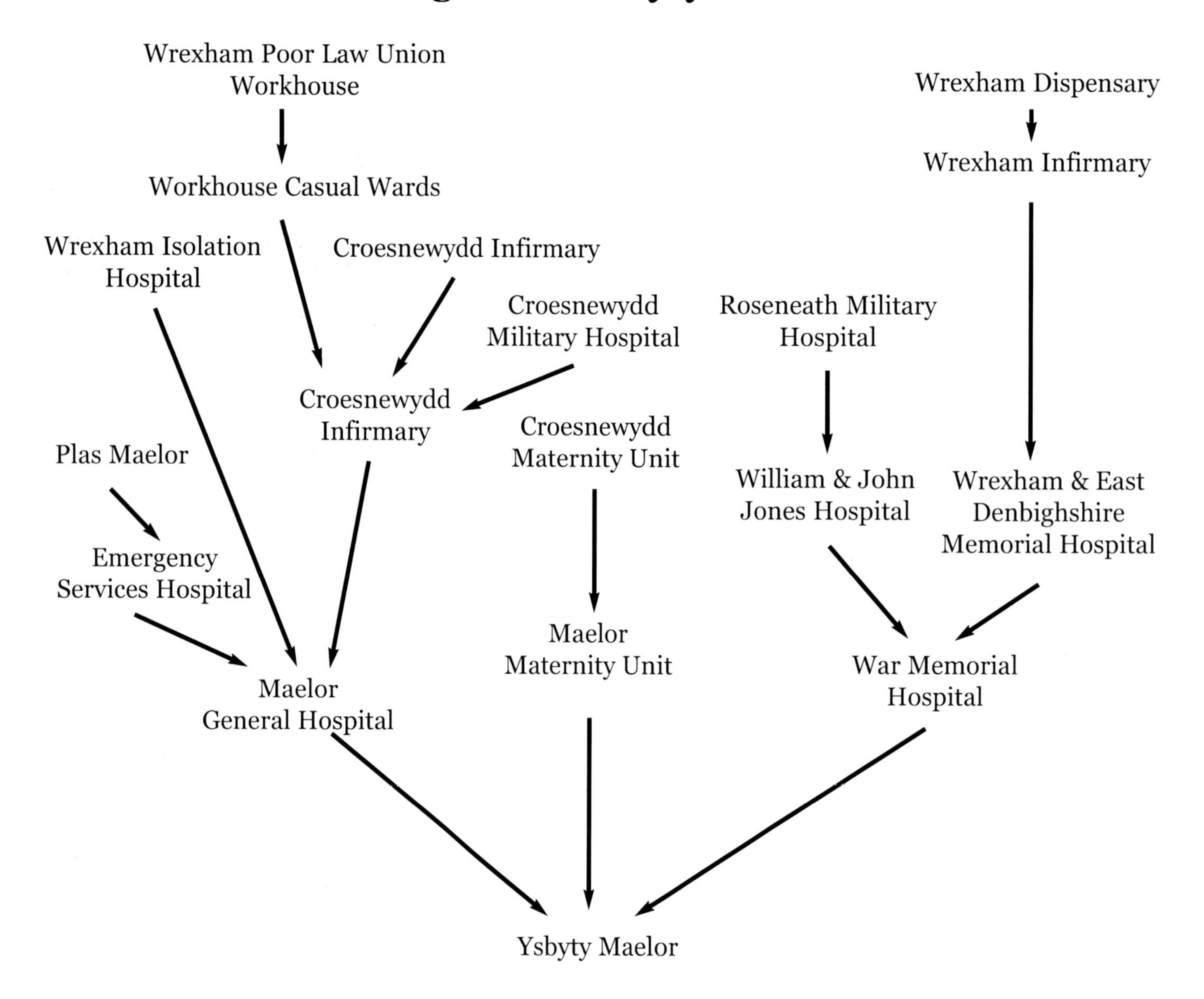

Chapter 1

THE WORKHOUSE

The Poor Law Relief Act, 1601

When this Act was introduced in 1601 paupers were made the responsibility of the local magistrates who appointed unpaid Overseers of the Poor for each parish; the church wardens of the area had the same powers as the overseers. The overseers were charged with ensuring that the poor were set to work or, if unfit for work, provided with relief, and to feed them in their homes. The funds for such relief (which was at the discretion of the overseers) came from (a) the Poor Rate, a sum levied on the inhabitants of the area, and (b) generous donations from the wealthier local inhabitants. The Poor Rate was levied by two local JPs who had the power to 'rate and tax' every inhabitant and occupier of houses, lands, tithes, under-woods, mines, etc. in the parish. In addition, these funds were used to ensure that there was a sufficient stock of flax and hemp, to enable the poor to be set to work, and also to pay for apprenticeships for older pauper children.

Persons who were in receipt of parish relief had to wear a large letter 'P' and the first letter of the parish, on the upper arm of the right sleeve, otherwise a magistrate might order their allowance to be 'abridged' or 'suspended' or the offender could be committed to the local house of correction and there set work to maintain themselves by hard labour.

There were three categories of poor and three levels of relief:

1. Those that were poor by impotency (through no fault of their own) which group included the aged, the decrepit, the lame, the blind, distracted persons (mentally ill) and infants. For these, the Overseers were to provide a necessary relief and an allowance.

2. Those who became poor due to casualty (accident) e.g. persons who had lost everything as a result of a fire, or who were overburdened by having too many children. If these people were of sufficient ability and strength, they were to be set work by the Overseers and to be further relieved according to their needs.

3. Those who made themselves poor by rioting, idleness, and drunkenness. These people were not allowed to be relieved, except in cases of great extremity, but were instead to be sent to the local House of Correction where they would be set to work in order to maintain themselves by hard labour.

If a single, or destitute woman, who was not from the parish, delivered a child, the overseers, (or the church wardens) had the right by law, to detain the woman in their custody until she could be conveyed to a justice of the peace, who would examine her, and commit her to the house of correction for a period not exceeding six months. The overseers were reimbursed for the cost of her care by the county or parish from where she had originally come.

Wrexham's first workhouse, 1737

As a result of the increasing demand for pauper relief, the Wrexham parish authorities were finding great difficulty in caring for the poor, and it was decided to set up a 'Poor House' (generally known as the 'Workhouse'), and a building was obtained in Salop Street, The Green, Wrexham (close to the site later occupied by the old gas works at the junction of Salop Road and Rivulet Road). This was part of the Wrexham Bridewell (gaol) and was financed from subscriptions paid by the big houses e.g. Erddig, Hafod-y-wern, Croesnewydd, The Mount and others. John Wood's 1833 map of Wrexham clearly shows where this building was situated.

The Workhouse was managed by a master and a matron, without any servants, with the female inmates carrying out all housework. The building included a small bedroom for the sick, the inmates tending one another, with the occasional attendance of a local doctor. Bedding and clothing were provided by the parish, and the workhouse master provided

An artist's impression of what Wrexham's first Bridewell and Workhouse, on the corner of Rivulet Road and Salop Road may have looked like. Drawn by the late John Bagshaw..

food at a fixed price per inmate, but he could also supplement this payment, by setting to work all able bodied paupers. The workhouse was fitted with looms and spinning wheels, which were under the charge of the master, but, by the late 1700s, trade conditions precluded the marketing of workhouse wares and all attempts at productive work by the workhouse inmates were abandoned

The workhouse could provide indoor relief for around eighty paupers and, according to one report, these included male and female 'lunatics, idiots, and imbeciles', who mixed during the day with the other inmates. In addition to these were those people who received outdoor relief, and at one time it is recorded that there were two hundred and ninety-seven individuals (including the families of thirty-seven militiamen) who were in receipt of relief in the Wrexham area.

Croesnewydd Workhouse

The Poor Law Amendment Act of 1837, aimed at preventing pauper discontent and the movement of the poor from parish to parish, established Poor Law Commissioners who recommended the combination of parishes into 'Unions' each of which was to be controlled by a Board of Guardians, elected by the rate payers within that Union area. The guardians in turn appointed overseers to collect the poor rates which were levied on the rate-payers of each area.

The Wrexham Board of Guardians held their first meeting on 31 March 1837 and decided to build a new workhouse, designed to accommodate over 500 inmates, on land at Croesnewydd. The land was purchased at a cost of £300 and with a total budget of just over £5,000 the workhouse was built the same year.

Meant to act as a deterrent, the workhouse provided living conditions that were less desirable than those of lower class labourers. The Guardians also provided relief to deserving people outside the workhouse in the form of money, food, and clothing.

In the spring and summer, the majority of the men worked the land, in the potato fields or in the fruit and vegetable gardens. Some of the less able inmates were put to work in the kitchen peeling potatoes — around 17 hundredweight was consumed each week. About sixteen of the more capable men were put to work as ward-men or helpers, carrying out domestic duties on the male wards, or dormitories. Inmates were also regularly employed in the tailor's shop, where clothing was made and repaired, or the shoe-makers shop, where the inmates shoes were made and repaired. Two or three inmates worked in the bakehouse while others helped in the boiler house attending to the steam boilers (Wrexham workhouse received between 30 and 40 tons of coal each week, delivered from Gate Wen Colliery by Davies Brothers). Approximately four inmates helped the gardener in the kitchen gardens and elsewhere. Sixteen men, including the mentally retarded, helped around the workhouse yards and offices. A pig-man was responsible for the feeding and care of the pigs and the hens, which played a very important role in the feeding of the inmates.

Females carried out general domestic work, giving help where required in the sick and infirm wards. Able bodied female inmates worked in the wash house and laundry, work which was recognised as being the hardest and most disagreeable in the whole establishment. Females also helped the sewing mistress, their main task being to repair the bed linen.

A school master and mistress were appointed who were responsible for the education of the workhouse children.

The porter acted as barber to the inmates and the lime-washer was responsible for painting the walls of the workhouse and out-buildings with lime.

Nurses were employed to care for the sick and infirm and, in the early days, were not trained, their only qualification

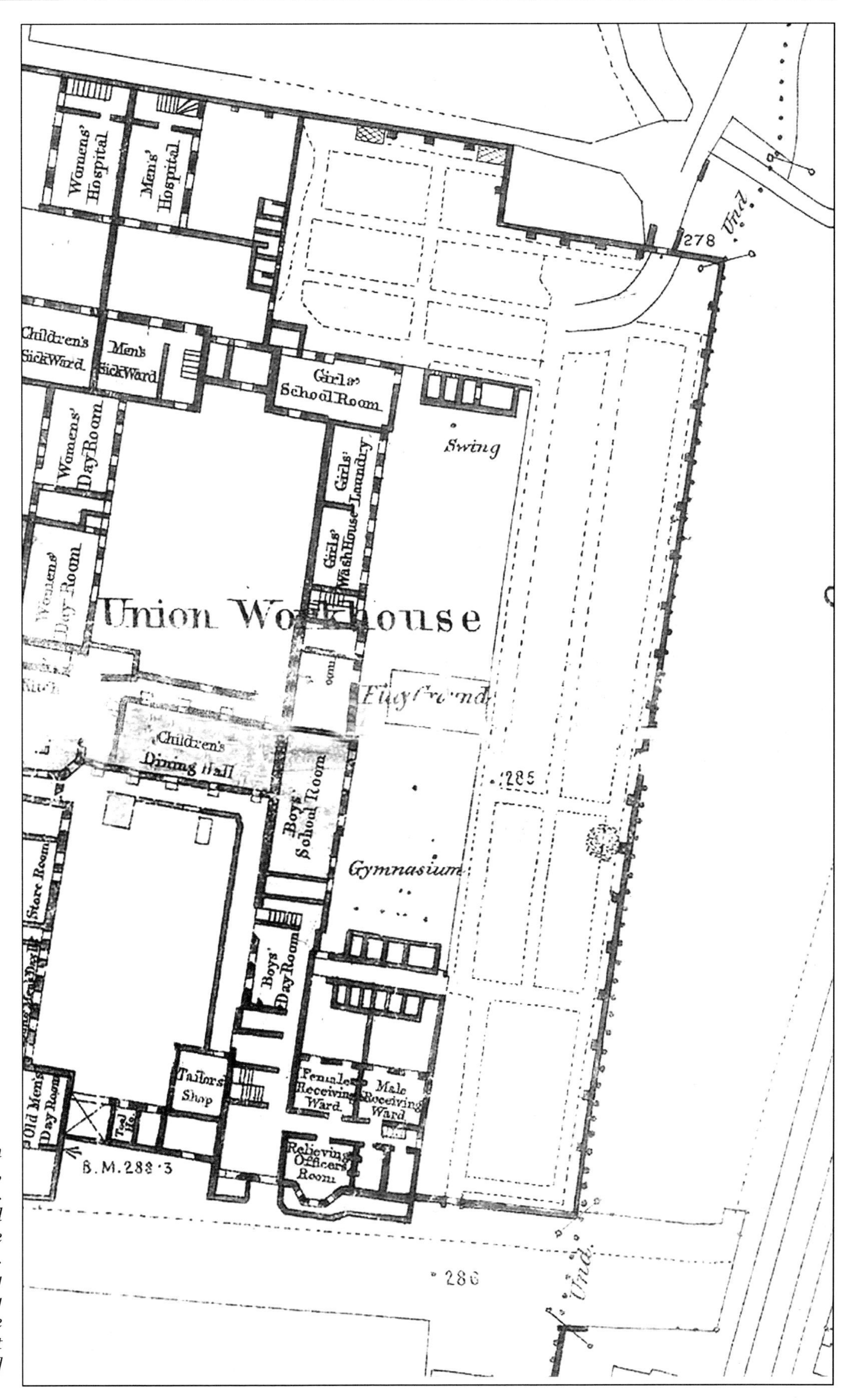

The OS plan of the Wrexham Union Workhouse in 1872., scale of 10"=1 mile. Unfortunately, this detailed plan only covers 50% of the actual workhouse buildings. The railway lines as they pass across the Watery Road level-crossing can be seen in the bottom right hand corner [WMS]

Wrexham Union Workhouse, 2005

The surviving workhouse buildings incorporated as part of Croesnewydd General Hospital. [WAWC]

Comparison of these photographs with the Ordnance Survey plans reproduced opposite would suggest that the surviving wing was not part of the original 1830s workhouse and was built in the late nineteenth century.

In the latter years of the workhouse, prior to the building being absorbed into the Maelor General Hospital, the ground floor of this block accommodated children with elderly sick males on the first floor.

Post the Second World War, this block has been used for paediatric care as part of the Maelor General Hospital and Ysbyty Maelor.

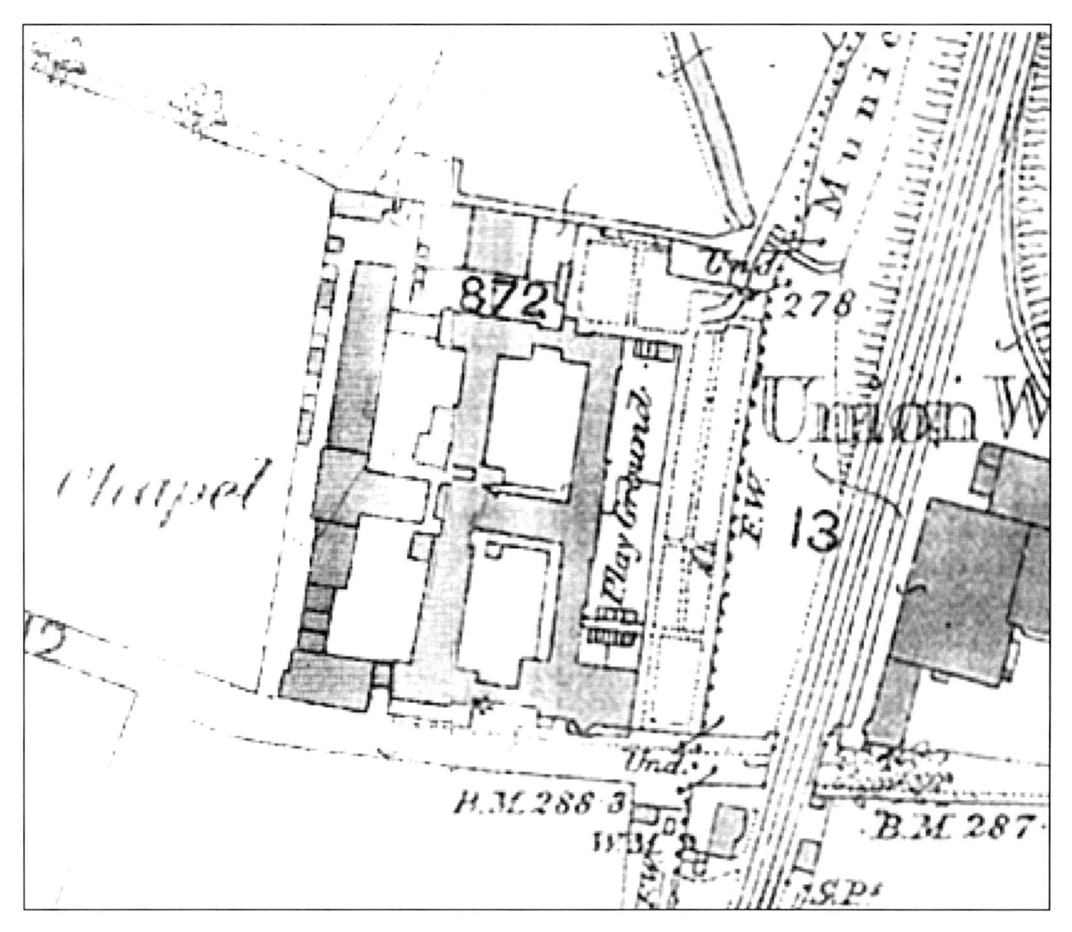

The full area of the workhouse can be seen on this smaller scale plan from 1874. Whilst not showing the same detail as the 1872 plan, it does show the entire building and clearly marks the original chapel which was in the centre of the west wing. [WMS]

This sketch was produced in the 1880s as part of a promotional leaflet for Wrexham's 'Jubilee Railway Station' (Central Station) and is the only known illustration of the Wrexham Union Workhouse before it was significantly altered by the building of what became the Croesnewydd Hospital. Watery Road runs L–R close to the bottom of the picture and the present-day railway signal box can be seen in the bottom right-hand corner. Either this sketch is highly inaccurate or a substantial part of the workhouse was demolished in the 1880s. The drawing of Cobden's Flour Mill on the right of the illustration, is reasonably accurate [WAWC]

being that they could read the directions written on a medicine bottle. However, it was reported in 1913 that there was a great improvement in the standard of care and expertise as the qualifications of the nurses had improved, a large percentage having received a full course of training. At the same time there was a great advance in the provision of equipment for the sick wards.

When the Midwives Act of 1902 came into force, the guardians insisted that at least one midwife was to be employed in the workhouse. She was required to be a person certified under the terms of the Act, who had passed the examination held by the Central Midwives Board and who held one of the certificates specified in Section 2 of the Act. All the treatment she prescribed was recorded, and she was responsible for notifying all her cases to her supervising authority.

Any inmate who refused or neglected to work would be deemed to be disorderly and was punished accordingly. No inmate, however, was required to undertake any work which the medical officer believed to be injurious to his or her health. All the inmates had to rise at 6.45am and go to bed at 8.00 pm.

Life in the workhouse was strictly regulated and the rules included the prohibition and disposal of 'articles not proper' to be brought in to the institute. Dice, letters, printed papers or articles of an obscene or improper nature, highly combustible articles, spirituous or fermented liquors were to be immediately confiscated. If an inmate was found to be in possession of money or any other valuables, they would be taken away and handed to the master, who would receive instructions from the Board of Guardians as to their disposal.

On admission every inmate was searched by an officer of the same sex, and prohibited articles were handed over to the Master who was required to make a record of any items of value in the Inmates Property Register. Unless inmates of the sick or lunatic wards, all adults and children had to be bathed on admission — unless the medical officer had given instruction to the contrary. All inmates were to be bathed at least once a month, but had the option of bathing once a fortnight if they wished. When preparing the bath the officer in charge was instructed to put cold water in the bath first, then hot water was added, to determine the temperature a thermometer was to be used the heat being not less than 80°F and not higher than 90°F. There was no privacy for the inmate at bath time, the paid officer was always to be present, part of his/her duties being to make a note of any bruises, marks, sores or whether the inmate was complaining of any pain or showing evidence of disease which had to be reported immediately to the matron or the master. Every hot water tap was provided with a key which was required to remain in the possession of the officer at all times. They were responsible for no hot water being used in their absence.

Every visitor had to give his or her name, and stated purpose of their visit to the porter before entering the gates. Infirmary patients could be visited on Mondays and Fridays between 2.00pm and 4.00pm. Workhouse inmates could have visitors on Mondays between the hours of 10am and 12 noon and between 2.00pm and 4.00pm but no patient or inmate could have more than three visitors at a time, and visitors could remain in the ward for 30 minutes only. Visitors under the age of 16 years were not allowed to visit anyone in the infirmary. Moving from one ward to the other was not allowed and it was strictly prohibited for any visitor to bring in food or liquor to any inmate in the institute. Any visitor bringing in alcohol, would render him or herself liable to a fine of £10, or a term of imprisonment, not exceeding two calendar months, for each offence. The only articles that could be brought into the workhouse were: flowers, sound oranges, good grapes, acid drops, biscuits, sweets, condensed milk, sugar, tea, new laid eggs and tobacco.

A set of regulations for the Wrexham Workhouse, signed by J. Bagnall Bury, Clerk to the Wrexham Board of Guardians, has survived and show that the inmates of the receiving wards, sick wards, lunacy wards and nurseries would be served their meals in their own wards, whilst all other classes would be served in the general dining hall.

Breakfast — 7.30–8.00am.
Dinner — 12noon–12.30.
Tea — 4.00pm–4.30pm.
Supper — 7.00–7.30pm.

All able bodied inmates were to work as directed by the master or the matron, from 8.00am–12noon, 1.00pm–4.00pm, 4.30–5.30pm daily except Sunday, Good Friday and Christmas Day.

In 1901–03, the majority of the inmates (1,363 people) were recorded as being destitute. A further 783 were deemed both sick and destitute. There were 99 deserted wives and children and 40 pregnant unmarried women (the majority of whom had previously been working in domestic service) who gave birth to 44 children in the workhouse. There were seven recorded orphaned children and 10 children admitted because their parents were in prison. The weak minded, idiotic, or insane totalled 79 people.

Staff

Master — G. S. Bessel £85 per annum.
Matron — Ellen Bessel £55 per annum

Chaplain — between 1891 and 1907, Canon W. H. Fletcher.
School-master and band-master — Peter Cartwright £50 per annum
School-mistress — Harriet Cartwright £32 per annum
Porter/barber — John Farthing £30 per annum
Portress and tramp mistress — M. E. Farthing £10 per annum
Food and accommodation were in addition to these salaries.

Other members of staff who were all paid 26/- (£1.30) per week included: laundress and labour mistress, two nurses, a tailor, a shoe-maker, a baker, a lime-washer and a boiler-man and fitter (who had to provide his own food).

Guardians Minute Book 1840.
There was a disagreement between the kitchen and medical staff, the query being 'whether a doctor should provide a bread poultice.' The answer was: 'That because the poultices were composed from household articles, they would not be provided [by a doctor].'

In February 1840, complaints were made regarding the conduct of the master. He was called before the Board of Guardians and informed that they were dissatisfied regarding the internal management of the workhouse, and that they had reason to believe that he was too much absent from it, and that he frequently returned in an improper state. He was cautioned.

In April 1840, the master of the workhouse reported that Ann Williams and Fanny Roberts, two girls of 15 years of age, had run away and were found in a 'house of bad fame' by the porter. It was ordered that they be sent to the aged female ward, and not be allowed animal food (meat) for the next two weeks, and to be put in separate solitary confinement for one hour each day.

May 1840 — a complaint was tabled at the meeting, which originated from several of the inmates, not being allowed a sufficient quantity of sound healthy potatoes at their meals owing to these being boiled in their skins, and the decayed parts not being cut out. At the same meeting, it was reported that a cutaneous disease (skin disease) had increased to a considerable extent amongst the girls of the workhouse, arising from the medical officers attention not having been called to the matter in time.

July 1840 — a complaint was entered in the visitors book calling attention to the fact that paupers were being conveyed to the place of interment on a 'common cart.' The clerk was directed to communicate with the contractor, stating that the Board of Guardians expects the dead to be taken by bearers to their place of interment, as specified in his contract.

August 1840 — at this meeting it was decided that able-bodied married women, widows, and their children, with young women of good character, be removed to rooms 80 and 8 to avoid contamination, and the degradation of associating with having bastard children, and other lewd and disorderly characters.

The Schoolroom

In 1877, the Board of Guardians obtained a further loan of £2,500 to build a schoolroom, and when the building was erected a schoolmaster and a schoolmistress was engaged to teach the workhouse children. In 1907 the workhouse school was closed and the children were sent to the elementary schools in the town. At this time there were 22 boys and 10 girls resident in the workhouse.

The Chapel

To provide a chapel within the workhouse grounds the guardians borrowed a further £500 on 6 October 1887. The old chapel can still be seen today having been incorporated within the hospital laundry and engineering departments of the Maelor Hospital (when you travel up Watery Road and reach the railway crossing, look to your right, approximately 15 yards or so along the railway, the building can be seen in a somewhat deteriorating condition with damaged stained-glass windows).

Child inmates

The children in the workhouse were deemed to be there through no fault of their own. Babies born there were registered as having been born at 'Plas Panton' in order not to have the stigma of the workhouse on their birth certificates.

Specific rules were laid down for the care of all youngsters. A medical officer was to examine all infants under the age of 18 months at least once a fortnight. Children over this age were examined every month, and a separate record card was kept on every child. On the 31 March 1915 a new ruling appeared which stated that all children over the age of 3

The doorway to the former children's home on Chester Street, now the offices of Walker, Smith & Way solicitors. [WAWC]

years had to leave the workhouse and placed in accommodation in Chester Street (until this time children had been allowed to stay at the workhouse until they were older). This house became Wrexham's first children's home. It was the former home of Dr Thomas Taylor Griffiths, a gentleman who was one of the founders of the town's first out-patients hospitals, the Wrexham Infirmary in Yorke Street, and the Ragged School on Hill Street, where the children of the poor were given a basic education without payment. This house was later used as the offices of the registrar of births, marriages and deaths and now houses a firm of solicitors.

In the workhouse registers it can be seen that, before 1915, when a child reached the age of 4 years he or she could be boarded out with various individuals. The majority of these children were either orphans or had been deserted by their parents and were aged between 4 and 12 years, and were of both sexes. The person taking the child into their care was given 3/- (15p) per week to cover the cost of their food and clothing. In 1871 it was recorded that one little girl of six years was boarded out to a carpenter and his wife and she was still with them in 1878 when she was 13 years of age. Some people took two children, especially if they were siblings. In 1871, two four-year old girls were boarded out to an Elizabeth Jones, a laundress of Llay, and the register shows they were still with her in 1878. However, that same year the register shows that they were transferred into the care of a Mrs White of Wrexham Regis. Another little girl aged 9 years was boarded out to a coal merchant at Allington in 1871 but in 1875 was transferred into the care of the same Mrs White. Many of the children who were boarded out, both boys and girls, were eventually transferred into the care of Mrs White who cared for nine children around this time. Further investigation revealed that Mrs White operated an orphans' school which trained children in domestic duties, giving them a better start when seeking employment, the boys were put into apprenticeship for one trade or another. In the late nineteenth century, Mrs White was operating a children's home in Greystones, a large property on the corner of Foster Road and Chester Road.

In 1921 the Chester Street Home was closed and the children were settled into homes in Little Acton which were purchased by the guardians. Again when the children became of a suitable age, they were placed in employment, mainly domestic service for girls and apprenticeships for boys, or other jobs where they could maintain themselves. The boys could also be sent to Canada under a government emigration scheme, but the guardians still kept oversight of their care and well being.

The following reports are typical of those sent to the Board of Guardians from the individual employers, with a written contribution from the boys.

James aged 17 years was placed in Laval County, Quebec.
Surroundings — good.
With present farmer — 3 years.
Health — good
Appearance — average, has grown considerably.
Has sufficient clothing.
Attends Church, but not day school.
Progress — good.
Character and behaviour, entirely satisfactory.
His terms were board and lodging and clothing, with 6 dollars a month.
The lad's progress is very marked, and that James was happy with the family.

Greystones, on the corner of Chester Road and Foster Road. [WAWC]

Jonathan aged 19 years placed with a farmer in Lincoln County, Ontario.
In a very good home.
Has good health.
Has been with present farmer for two years.
Attends Church and Sunday school.
Progress — good.
Behaviour — excellent.
His terms were board with 15 dollars per month in winter and 22 dollars in the summer.
Jonathan is in charge of his own affairs, and while not making any complaints, he thinks he can do with more money. He will make change soon. His employer classified him, as a good and honourable lad, with no bad habits.

In the 1930s, the workhouse children were housed on the ground floor of the building which later became the paediatric department of the Maelor General Hospital, on the Croesnewydd side of the road. In the upstairs wards were some of the old and infirm workhouse inmates who were bed ridden and required nursing care. The children were cared for in the nursery from birth to the age of four years. Any sick babies or children were segregated from the others, and put into a smaller ward where extra care could be given and, when they recovered, would be returned to the nursery. The matron and the medical officer, kept a very strict eye on this department. The Infirmary nurses, worked here to gain experience in the care of children and babies. The children would be taken for walks when possible, to get fresh air. Babies were put in perambulators, and pushed around the grounds. They were helped with feeding, and kept clean and tidy. The majority of these children had been abandoned and it was very difficult for nurses not to become attached to them. When the infants reached the age of 4 years, they were transferred to a children's home in the Wrexham area. The majority of workhouse children, whether male or female, were dressed in blue smock-type dresses with white collars.

Older members of the community will probably recall, when passing through the gates of Croesnewydd Hospital from the direction of Maesgwyn Road, a large wall on the left side of the driveway which enclosed orchards and vegetable gardens, which were tended by the inmates of the old workhouse. These inmates resided in the casual ward building. There were also piggeries, and places where chickens were kept near the boiler rooms and the railway line. The fruit and vegetable gardens were later turned into a car park.

In 1920 a government inspector visited the workhouse and wrote a damning report, stating that the premises were practically unchanged over the previous 80 years, and were in a state of senile decay. 'The building is roughly built, the walls are unplastered and the wards are badly ventilated. There is no damp course, and the floors in many parts are worn, and harbour dust and dirt. Most of the windows are of iron'. The inspector also reported his concern about fire hazards, and the spartan conditions under which the paupers were forced to exist in the dormitories, which were cold, cheerless and badly ventilated. The day rooms were depressing with flagged and tiled floors. Heating was by means of antiquated fireplaces. The staircases were dark, narrow, awkward, and in a dilapidated condition, quite unsuitable for the aged and infirm. He summed up his report by saying that the building was dilapidated and obsolete, and would cost £10,000 to modernise. Such expenditure would give a fresh lease of life to a building which was no longer suitable for the purpose for which it was first built. At the time of the report, there were 242 inmates in the workhouse, and 32 tramps in the vagrants section. Among the inmates there were 17 lunatics or feeble minded persons, and 50 bedridden patients in the infirmary.

The minutes of the Wrexham Board of Guardians for May 1926 show that they were in serious financial trouble and had declared themselves bankrupt, with a bank overdraft of £59,301-10s.-3d. This overdraft had increased to £65,000 by November of the same year.

The Board of Guardians was abolished by an Act of Parliament of 1929 and their responsibilities were taken over by Denbighshire County Council, as part of the provisions of the Public Assistance Act (later the National Assistance Act, 1948). County councils were instructed to look into the need to replace workhouses and Denbighshire County Council planned the first purpose-built public assistance institute in the country, to be sited on 11 acres in the fields on the opposite side of the road to the old workhouse. Its buildings were intended to provide accommodation for the old and the infirm, the mentally slow and those not needing skilled or regular medical attention. It was for the welfare of old folk 'who, in the eventide of their

Student nurse Gwyneth Davies with some young patients from the children's ward and the workhouse, 1939.

lives, are compelled owing to their circumstances to seek a home and the necessary comforts of life from the County Council'. Children were already being catered for at homes in Little Acton. It was with this aim in mind that Plas Maelor was built in 1934.

The Casual Wards

Tramps and vagrants sought food and shelter daily and, as the demand increased, the Board of Guardians secured a loan of £1,000 on 21 November 1872 to purchase an area of land adjacent to the workhouse. A second loan of £1,000 was secured on 24 July 1873 and used to erect casual (or receiving) wards to accommodate vagrants and tramps. A further top-up loan was obtained in August 1885 to complete the work.

The casual ward had 16 cells as sleeping accommodation for men, as well as a separate ward, which had eight hammocks, which could be slung up to provide sleeping quarters for the better class of vagrant. In the female section there were 6 cells.

On the land where the Maelor Hospital stands today, were fields which the Board of Guardians rented, in which potatoes were planted for the workhouse. Tramps would work in the fields during the day, and they were allowed food and a bed for the night. Prior to their discharge the following day, the able bodied men were given the task of breaking around 3 hundredweight of stone, before being set free for the road again. These broken stones were sold to the Wrexham Rural District Council. Those tramps who were not capable of carrying out heavy work were given wood to saw or chop. During the winter months, when there was no work to be done in the fields, and the demand for firewood was high, all men worked in the wood sheds, sawing and chopping timber.

Anyone believed to be genuinely in search of work, would be discharged immediately after breakfast, to enable them to seek work at a respectable time.

The original casual wards were replaced by new buildings in the 1930s. It would appear that some residents were still living here in the 1940s and helped out with odd jobs and the maintenance of the hospital grounds. These people were eventually moved to Greenacres, a home in Rhosddu (next door to St James's Church), under the care of Gwyn and Lena Jones.

Chapter 2

CROESNEWYDD INFIRMARY

On 10 December 1896 the Wrexham Board of Guardians purchased a plot of land adjoining the workhouse complex for £1,600. On 2 November 1905, a loan of £12,339 was obtained for building a new infirmary on this site. Alterations and additions were made to the existing workhouse at the same time. A further loan of £1,300 was secured in February 1908 in order to furnish the new infirmary.

The infirmary at the workhouse was opened in October 1908, with the intention of caring for the sick inmates and local people of the area, whilst also providing maternity care — mainly for unmarried mothers or destitute women as most married women had their babies delivered in their own homes.

The entrance door to the new infirmary faced Maesgwyn Road, and on entering the hospital, to the right of the corridor were the labour wards, and opposite these were the maternity ward and nursery. Next to these were stairs and a manual lift, leading up to Female 1, the ward which catered for gynaecological, surgical and medical cases. The ground floor corridor continued from the maternity area, to the theatre and a little further on the left-hand side, the staff dining room. Opposite these, were stairs which led to the matron's office, and a further set of stairs led from here to another floor above.

Returning to the ground floor corridor, which passed the nurses' dining room, Male Ward 1 was on the left, and the adjacent stairs led up to Male Ward 2. Near the stairs was situated a manual lift, with pulley ropes, which had to be pulled by the attendant, to elevate the patient to the upper floor. If the patient was a stretcher case, carrying their weight and negotiating the bend in the stairs could be difficult at times.

Croesnewydd Hospital did not function for very long before its work was interrupted by the outbreak of the First World War, and part of the hospital was taken over to serve as the Croesnewydd Military Hospital. Some of these soldiers were cared for at Roseneath which was also converted to a military hospital. Those cases needing surgery would have been admitted to Croesnewydd. The First World War casualties who were admitted to hospitals in Britain were soldiers who had already been patched up in casualty clearing stations (close to the front line) and field hospitals (in the rear of the British lines) before being transported back to Britain. Many of the injured would have died on the way.

The following information was obtained from the admissions register for 1914–8 war casualties.

1 November 1914 — 101 admissions — Belgian troops from the 5th, 6th, 7th, 10th,14th, *regiments de ligne, chasseurs,and grenadiers*. All were catholics, and were probably casualties of the Battle of Mons. They were suffering from bullet, shrapnel, and shell wounds.

3 April 1915 — 71 admissions — British soldiers, suffering from abcesses, rheumatic fever,

The doctors, matron, nurses, Red Cross staff and army staff at the Military Hospital. It would appear that the same staff worked in both the Croesnewydd and Roseneath hospitals. [WAWC]

Croesnewydd Infirmary, 2005

The surviving original 1908 hospital buildings incorporated as part of Croesnewydd/Maelor General Hospital. [WAWC]

The above photograph shows how the old workhouse building (right) was linked to the Croesnewydd Infirmary building and later formed part of the Maelor General Hospital.

The south-east view of the rear of the Croesnewydd Infirmary building. In later years the building on the left housed Gilliat maternity ward (upstairs) and Bonney gynaecology ward (downstairs). Bonney Ward extended into the ground floor of the building on the right, with Blairbell ante-natal ward above.

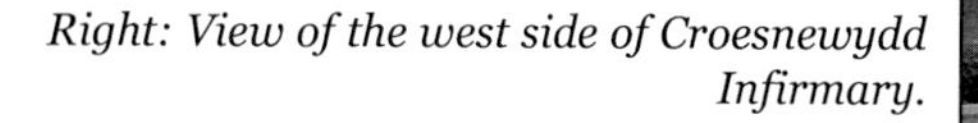

Right: View of the west side of Croesnewydd Infirmary.

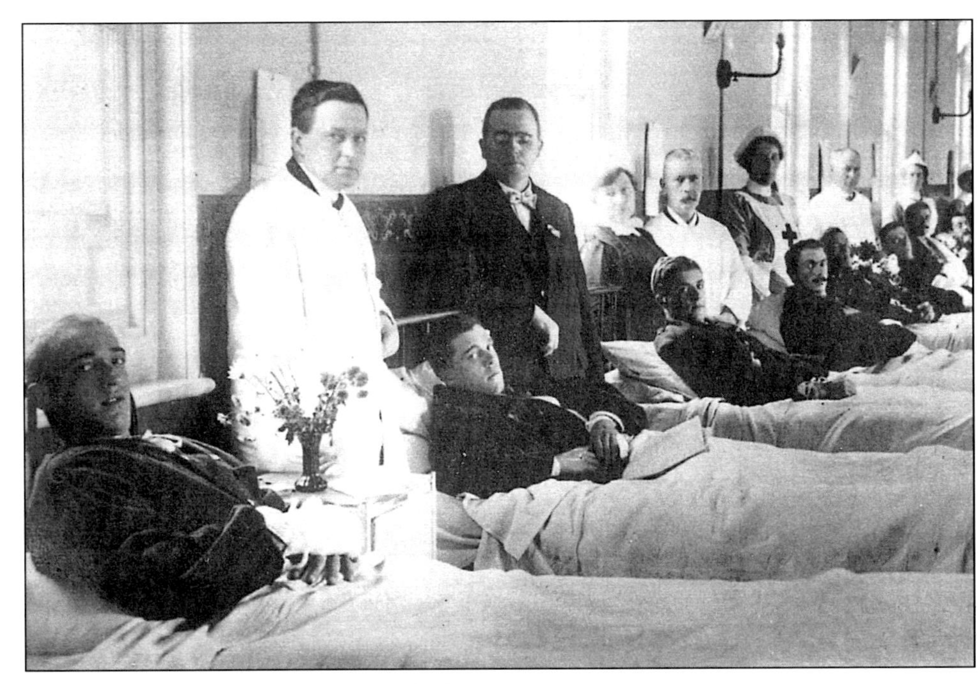

Wounded soldiers recovering in the Croesnewydd Military Hospital [WAWC]

deafness, gastro-enteritis, VDH (valvular heart disease) bronchitis, bullet wounds and a back injury due to a kick from a horse.

May 1915 — 51 admissions — possibly from the Battle of Ypres where poison gas was used for the first time otherwise much the same — gun shot and shrapnel wounds, a few knee injuries. Three local men were suffering from frostbite. Eight of the soldiers were serving with the Royal Welsh Fusiliers.

26 October 1915 — 124 admissions — injuries similar to those already mentioned, but it was now noticed that loss of hearing, nervous debilities and knee problems were complained of.

January–June 1916 — 74 admissions — over this period of time trench foot and more debilitating conditions were noted .

8–9 July 1916 — further admissions — one young soldier with shrapnel wounds to his back, died the day after admission, he had given twenty one months service, seven months in the field of battle. Another twenty year old soldier admitted had amputation of his left arm and died a few weeks later. There were four deaths during this period of time. Trench fever, para typhoid and cholera was now recorded amongst the admissions.

14 September 1916 — 30 admissions — conditions more or less the same.

October 1916 — 7 admissions — suffering from mainly debilitating conditions e.g. boils, impetigo, sores, scarlet fever. There was one death due to a stomach condition.

November 1916 — 90 admissions — debilitating conditions were now more pronounced, and was the poor physique of the patients.

February–March 1917 — few admissions — most with debilitating conditions.

April–May 1917 — 125 admissions — mainly debilitating conditions.

June –July 1917 — few admissions.

6 August 1917 — 128 admissions — 52 with gas poisoning, laryngitis and conjunctivitis (all caused by poison gas). The others were suffering from trench fever, and gun shot wounds.

October 1917 — 111 admissions — these casualties were possibly from the Battle of Ypres, suffering from war wounds.

November–December 1917 — 106 admissions — suffering from war wounds , trench fever, and trench foot.

January–August 1918 — 212 admissions — mainly suffering from gun shot, shrapnel and shell wounds.

September 1918 — 67 admissions — several of these soldiers were suffering from mustard gas injuries, the first time for this injury to be entered in the register as ‘Shell Gas (Mustard) injuries’. 27 Canadian soldiers were also admitted with gun shot and shrapnel wounds.

November–December 1918 — 32 admissions — similar injuries to September.

January—February 1919 — 54 admissions — conditions much the same.

The last discharge from Croesnewydd Military Hospital was on 29 March 1919. The total casualties received from 1914 to 1919 was 1,732 of which 10 died and 11 had limbs amputated.

Soldiers with amputated limbs were wheeled around the grounds by nurses or orderlies to help relieve the boredom and get some fresh air. Some coughed incessantly from gas-damaged lungs and others had severe nerve damage and were unable to lead normal lives ever again. Some had severe head and facial injuries which again impaired their quality of life.

Croesnewydd Infirmary became a training school for nurses in 1908. In 1986 Nurse Matthias, in her ninety-first year, recalled her period as a nurse at Croesnewydd. Any young lady wishing to train in nursing had to be twenty-one years of age, and the training period was three years. In 1916 Miss Matthias commenced her general training in Croesnewydd Infirmary, there being no State Registered Nurses at that time. Her salary was 15/- (75p) per month. Two months of her training was given to the care of the wounded soldiers, the rest to caring for the general patients in the Infirmary, and doing night duty. After 3 years training she became a qualified general nurse

Left: 1939, some of the last group of student nurses to train at Croesnewydd Infirmary. Second from the right is Mary Smith. They were used to nurse wounded soldiers in order to gain experience.

She then went to a private hospital in Swansea, as a private nurse so that she could raise £30 which was the sum of money required to pay for her midwifery training, which took 6 months. She qualified as a midwife at the Lovedale Hospital, Birmingham in 1922 then took the Queen's District Nurse Training at Kirby Street, Liverpool (six months with no pay). She was based at the nurses home and had to walk to all her calls, which were in a very poor, and rough part of Liverpool. After obtaining the Queen's District Nurse qualification, she continued general and midwifery nursing for a while, and then became a district nurse/midwife in Kettering, Northhamptonshire, where she travelled to her calls by bicycle. She returned to Wrexham in 1934, aged 40, and worked for the Gwersyllt District Nurses Association, covering 11 districts, until she retired in 1961.

By 1938 the age for entry into nurse training in Wrexham had come down to 18 years when young ladies applying to take training were to be well educated, and were required to be medically examined by the medical officer of the hospital. A written educational examination was to be taken at the War Memorial Hospital after which, before an applicant was accepted for the three year training, she had to serve three months in the wards during which time the Public Assistance Committee could terminate her service at any time. During this three month trial the applicant had to supply her own uniform. On completion of this initial probationary period, she would be paid £30 per annum for the first year, £35 for the second year and £40 for the third year. Nurses were provided with in-door uniform and their washing was done free of charge.

Probationers were liable to be suspended from duty at any time by the matron, for misconduct or neglect of duty, in which case they were not entitled to receive notice prior to leaving, or any pay in lieu of notice. The matron had to report any such suspension to the Public Assistance Committee, who had power to discharge probationers.

The students were given one day off per month, and had to queue up outside the matron's office to get a pass to release them from the hospital and allow them to return without problems. At this time the matron was a Miss Nellie Parry, a very strict disciplinarian, who was not averse to personally demonstrating how a job was to be carried out. General nurse training lasted for three years, during which time the trainee gained experience in surgery, medicine and gynaecology at Croesnewydd. Other specialised training was available at the Wrexham & East Denbighshire War Memorial Hospital.

The maternity wards remained in the same place as they were during the workhouse era. Dr John (Jock) Reid was the medical officer in charge of all cases in Croesnewydd with Mr Robert Owen Jones, the county obstetrician and gynaecologist with direct control over midwifery and gynaecology. Miss Nellie Parry continued to serve as matron and continued to work extremely hard. If a domestic was not, in her opinion, cleaning an area properly, she was not averse to taking over the task herself. Croesnewydd catered for low risk maternity cases but sometimes these did develop complications and instrument deliveries did take place there. High risk maternity cases were taken to Ruabon County

A badly damaged photograph showing the staff of Croesnewydd Hospital in 1941.

This block, alongside Watery Road, was opened in the 1930s close to the site of the former casual wards and the relieving officer's room of the old workhouse. They now accommodate the Estates Office of Ysbyty Maelor. [WAWC]

Above: 1950s. Nurse W. Baker takes the temperature, blood pressure
and pulse of a long-stay male patient on the balcony outside Male Ward 2.
Left: 1950s. A patient on Female Ward 1 is presented with a bouquet on the occasion of her 100th birthday by the ward sister.

Maternity Hospital between 1935 and 1947, after which they went to Trevalyn Manor Maternity Hospital.

Croesnewydd Infirmary also cared for geriatric and chronically sick patients. By the 1930s, maternity cases were accommodated on the ground floor, close to the Maesgwyn Road entrance as was Female Ward 1, which catered for geriatric and chronically sick. On the first floor were Male Wards 1 & 2, also catering for geriatric and chronically sick patients.

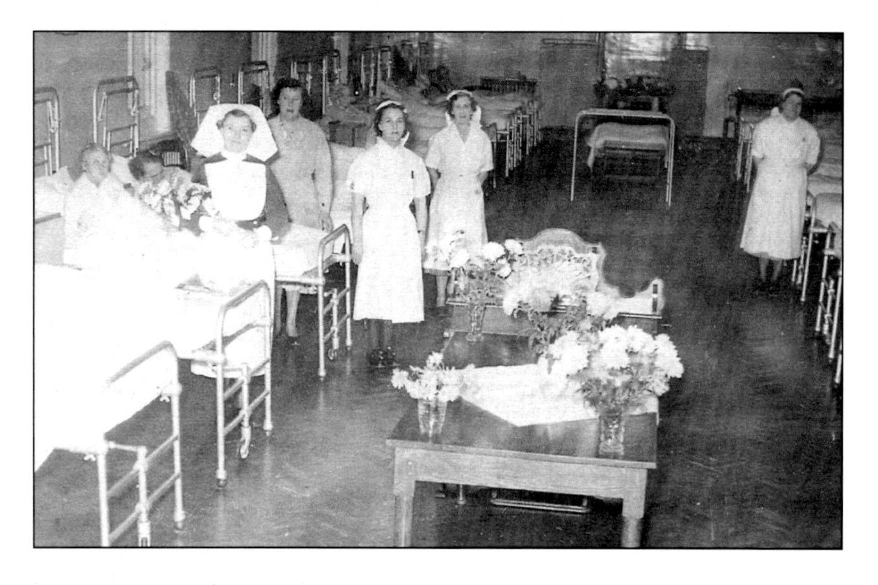

Above: 1940s. Sister Randles, senior midwifery sister, Croesnewydd. A porter's trolley can be seen on the right. [John Randles]

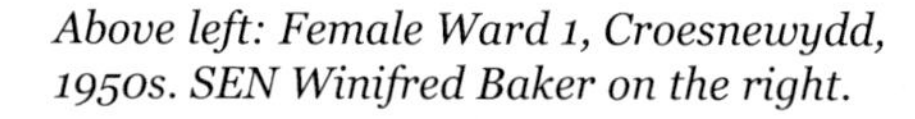

Above left: Female Ward 1, Croesnewydd, 1950s. SEN Winifred Baker on the right.

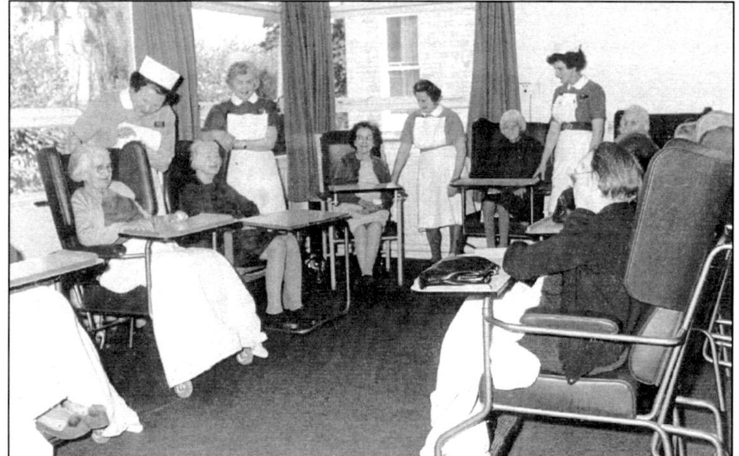

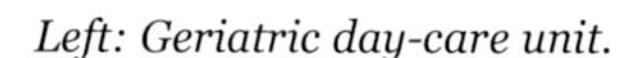

Left: Geriatric day-care unit.

Above: The old Croesnewydd Hospital chapel, alongside the railway line, now part of the hospital engineering department. [WAWC]

Left: Corrugated iron buildings at Croesnewydd Infirmary used in later years as a nurses' canteen and changing room. [WAWC]

Chapter 3

Wrexham Fever (Isolation) Hospital

Two fever wards were presented to Wrexham Infirmary (see Chapter 6) in 1866 by Mr William Overton, their function being to isolate patients suffering from infectious diseases. The building was located at the rear of the Infirmary. In 1881,the wards were closed and converted into a new outpatients department and a dispensary. Some time later, an area of land known as Cae Margaret Halcyn was purchased to the west of the Croesnewydd Workhouse and in 1900 a new fever hospital was built there under the supervision of the Joint Fever Hospital Committee.

The Fever Hospital was cordoned off from Croesnewydd Workhouse by a high wall which enclosed it within its own grounds. At the entrance was a large gate which was locked at all times. Access was gained by ringing a bell on the gate which was then opened by a porter.

The hospital was constructed of red Ruabon brick. The 'house-like' building on the left of the main gate was the nurses residence where, at one time, the matron also lived. On the right of the main gate was a lodge where the senior porter lived. Behind the lodge was the night nurses' residence.

In the early years the Fever Hospital was run by the Wrexham Rural District Council and seems to have been under the care of Dr Moss. The 1912 report shows that the matron was Miss M. Bushnall and the medical officers were Dr Moss and Dr T. Roberts. In about 1923 Dr T. P. Edwards was appointed medical officer. He later became medical officer for Wrexham Borough and retired in 1951. In the late 1920s, a Matron Davies was appointed to take charge of the hospital with Sister Humphreys as her deputy.

In 1986 and elderly lady from Johnstown recalled that, in 1912, her brother, the late Dr Thomas William Jones, having trained at Liverpool University, had his first appointment as surgeon at the Fever Hospital. Whilst there his duties included performing tracheotomies (probably on diptheria cases, when a grey membrane covered the back of the throat obstructing the patients breathing) and acting as anaesthetist for Dr Moss. Dr Jones left for military service in 1916, attached to the 27th Bn Northumberland Fusiliers, and was killed on 11 March 1917, aged 31, whilst attending to a wounded soldier in the Battle of Arras, France.

The author's mother recalled both herself and her sister contracting scarlet fever in about 1916/17 during an epidemic of the disease. Beds at the Fever Hospital were in short supply and they both had to share the same bed.

The main building was an elevated, stilt-like structure, with many windows and a covered verandah all around it. Patients were able to stand here, sheltered from the weather, and talk to their relatives through the windows. On a patient's discharge, all toys, books or clothing remained in the hospital for incineration in an effort to prevent the spread of disease.

The hospital had a total of six wards with approximately 108 beds, each ward caring for different diseases e.g. diptheria ward, scarlet fever ward and typhoid ward.

The hospital had its own kitchen and special ambulance staff who did not come into contact with staff from the other hospitals. When going off duty all staff had to remove their uniform and place it in a staff laundry bins before washing thoroughly and putting on their own clothes. A former colleague of the author's worked in the Fever Hospital for over ten years during the 1930s and 1940s. She remembered Dr T. P. Edwards giving lectures to students on infectious

The original porter's lodge which was later used as accommodation for the matron. [WAWC]

Nurses' home at the Fever Hospital, photographed in 2005.. [WAWC]

diseases. Even if they had been working the night shift, they had to attend the lectures in the morning before going to bed. Amongst the diseases that she recalled being nursed at the hospital were anthrax and a twelve-year old dying of congenital syphilis. Children also regularly died of diptheria. During the Second World War the hospital admitted 238 cases of cerebral spinal meningitis in two years, several of the patients were soldiers. There was a male and a female ward for these cases. Infectious cases were accompanied by a nurse from their home in the hospital's ambulance (driven in the 1940s by Mr Davies). During the 1940s the Night Sisters were Sister Hughes and Sister Forbes and Senior SEN I. Roberts who worked a duty rota. Whilst on duty they had to write a report on each ward which was presented to the matron in the morning. The hospital physiotherapist was Mr Pratt.

Steam tents were regularly used in the treatment of diptheria. Screens were erected around the patient's bed or cot which would then be covered with sheets. A steam kettle with an elongated spout and a fan-shaped diffuser which directed the steam through the sheets at the back of the bed, maintaining an even temperature of 75° F. This treatment was used if the patient had a tracheotomy as it was important that the air was warmed before entering the trachea.

Staff meals were taken in the staff dining room. All staff had to remain standing until the matron or her deputy arrived and said grace.

Between the late 1940s and the 1960s the matron was Miss Jane Saunders who moved to live in the porters lodge. She was a formidable and strict matron who, assisted by her secretary, paid the staff wages from the window of the lodge.

During the 1950s there was a large polio epidemic in the Wrexham area and additional iron lungs had to be borrowed from other hospitals to supplement the Fever Hospital's two iron lungs. Medical and nursing staff were stretched to capacity, some doing double shifts, to enable the hospital to cope. Intensive care was carried out around the clock and only three patients died.

In the late 1950s the number of fever cases fell dramatically due to the introduction of antibiotics and, gradually the wards were closed until, in the 1960s, only one remained open, named Bromfield, which was divided into cubicles. After a patient was discharged the cubicle windows were closed, the doors sealed and the area fumigated. After 24 hours, all the windows were opened and the cubicle left for some time before the domestics came in to wash the walls, floor and furniture.

The former Fever Hospital wards were

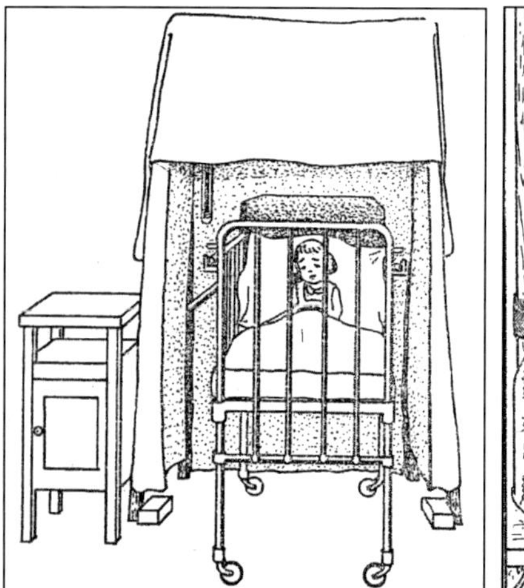

Above: Sketch of a steam tent and the steam kettle used in the treatment of diptheria.

Right: Iron lung similar to those used at Wrexham. They were used in the cases of paralysis of the chest muscles, for the prolonged administration of artificial respiration, by means of an electric motor and bellows which alternately increase and decrease the air pressure within the airtight iron lung. There are portholes on either side to allow nurses to attend to the patient.

One of the surviving isolation wards at the Fever Hospital, photographed in 2005.. Amongst the original buildings was a mortuary for the exclusive use of the Fever Hospital. [WAWC]

transferred to the care of the elderly and chronic sick. Bromfield Isolation Unit continued to function, under the supervision of the matron of the Maelor General Hospital, until 1996 when these services were transferred to the main hospital buildings. After almost a century of health care, some of these buildings were demolished in 1997 and the others used for non-patient care purposes.

Matron Saunders retired in August 1962.

Reminiscences of Mrs Margaret Jones, a domestic supervisor at the Fever Hospital

Margaret Jones and her sister both worked as domestics at the Wrexham Fever Hospital, their main duties being to clean the wards but they also had to boil the patient's crockery, doing one ward at a time. Margaret was promoted from domestic to matron's personal maid. She started her day at 7.30am, worked until 2pm when she was given a two hour break before working until 8pm. She had one day off each week. Her main duties were to clean the matron's bungalow, attend to the laundry and serve the matron's meals. She woke the matron each morning with a cup of tea then collected her breakfast from the kitchen which she then had to keep warm until she heard a hand bell which signalled that matron had arrived in the dining room and was ready for breakfast. Everything had to be set out correctly. When the matron had finished eating, she would ring a bell for Margaret to come and clear everything away.

Margaret was always nervous of the matron, and really tried her best to please her. One day, when she was cleaning and polishing the sitting room, she accidentally knocked over a fine cut-glass fruit bowl which smashed into fine pieces. Absolutely panic stricken, and knowing matron would be extremely annoyed, she could not wait to get off duty quickly enough. When 2pm came she rushed into Wrexham to buy a replacement but, of course, this was impossible as her wages were very poor and a replacement would have cost her two or three months wages. She bought what she thought looked almost like the bowl and rushed it back to the bungalow. A few days later she was summoned to matron's sitting room and, shaking from head to toe, had to face her wrath. After explaining what had happened, she was told how stupid she had been and that she should have come to her as soon as the bowl had been broken.

An indistinct newspaper photograph of Mr Sidney Aston, chairman of the Maelor Hospital House Committee presenting Matron Saunders with a transistor radio as her retirement gift in 1962.

Chapter 4

PLAS MAELOR

Plas Maelor was designed by Gilbert D. Wiles, the Denbighshire County Architect and was the first institution of its kind to be erected by any county council.

At Croesnewydd, the existing boiler house, plant house with generators and calorifiers, laundry, etc. were utilised to provide the basic services for Plas Maelor, thus not detracting from the amenities of the new site. The building was built with local brick and roofed with Welsh slate, with attractive gardens and lawns. The land to the rear of the building was converted into a fruit orchard.

The buildings consisted of two pavilions for men on one side of the administration block and two pavilions for women on the other side. The whole complex was connected by a 530ft long corridor. Each pavilion contained accommodation for 68 people, and there were six sleeping wards for eight people in each, and five sleeping wards with four persons in each. Two day rooms were provided, with the usual offices. The wards were deliberately small 'so as to ensure such proper classification that would add to the comfort of the residents'. When functioning fully Plas Maelor was able to cater for 276 elderly people.

The Central Administration Block contained a dining hall, kitchen and stores, with a staff dining room, sitting room and bedrooms. In the grounds, separate buildings housed the master's residence, the engineer's residence, the porter's lodge (with inquiry office), and a reception block with accommodation for 6 men and 6 women in separate wards. All equipment was of the most modern and up-to-date type. The council also arranged for there to be facilities for the reception of wireless broadcasts. Inmates were to be drawn from Llansilin D.C., Chirk D.C., Llangollen D.C., plus the urban districts as well as Wrexham Borough and Rural Districts.

Plas Maelor was opened in 1934 by the Rt Hon. David Lloyd George, MP. It functioned until the Second World War broke out in 1939, when, in anticipation of war casualties, it was requisitioned by the War Office and converted into an Emergency Medical Services (EMS) Hospital. The residents were transferred to Morda, Welshpool, Forden, New Hall (Ruabon) etc., until the end of the war. When hostilities were over, Plas Maelor was handed back to the Denbighshire County Council.

Plas Maelor, Wrexham, 1934.

Emergency Services Hospital 1939–45 (Plas Maelor)

When the Second World War broke out in 1939 contingency plans were made for coping with the anticipated casualties and Plas Maelor was converted into an Emergency Military Services Hospital (EMS). Military doctors and a few military nurses arrived, but the running of the hospital came under Croesnewydd Matron Nellie Parry and Assistant Matron Sarah Williams. Some of the Croesnewydd nurses were transferred to the EMS and, with the added invaluable help of the Wrexham Red Cross and St John's nurses, it functioned very efficiently.

Dr John Marchant, an RAF medical officer, was transferred to the EMS from Liverpool but it was the early summer of 1940 before the first casualties arrived having been wounded during the battle for France and the evacuation from Dunkirk. Dr Marchant, recalls that these casualties were not badly injured, but were poorly enough to be kept in hospital. Dr Marchant was transferred away from Wrexham in 1942/3 but returned after his demobilisation, living in Chirk and working in the Wrexham hospitals as a consultant anaesthetist until his retirement.

Mr Ninian came to the EMS, possibly around 1942, as a military surgeon and, at the end of the war, continued to work at the Maelor Hospital as the senior medical officer until his retirement.

The military patients, when up and about, wore blue serge suits with red ties, and some of the older residents of the community will probably remember them when they came into the town, to the shops, or for entertainment.

The guard room was on the right hand side of the main gate of the Maelor Hospital, opposite where the pathology laboratory is today.

All soldiers in the Second World War had their blood grouped. The information on their tags was name, number and religion. On the battlefields there were clearance areas, dug outs or even a tent two or three miles behind the front line where casualties were assessed. The soldiers were patched up and either returned to duties or were transferred to the nearest military hospital, quite often on intravenous plasma which saved the patient from dying from shock brought on by severe blood loss.

Blood, if required for the British troops, would be given on arrival at the military hospital having been delivered from Britain. After the new technique of the closed sterile method of collection was introduced, many lives were saved. This permitted blood to be collected in one location, stored and then transported to distant field hospitals for transfusion to a wounded soldier. This was a facility unavailable to the German Army which was supplied with

The Emergency Services Hospital at Plas Maelor, Wrexham, 1940. [Dr Marchant]

The Emergency Services Hospital at Plas Maelor, Wrexham, 1940. The crowded nature of the ward would suggest that this was taken after the admission of the wounded from the campaign in France. [Dr Marchant]

Wrexham Red Cross volunteer ambulance drivers during the Second world War. Photographed in front of the old 1887 chapel. During the 1940s, Wrexham Civil Defence Corps stored its equipment in these buildings.
[Late Miss Molly Preen]

colloid and periston. In 1943 penicillin was first made available to British soldiers and DDT powder was also introduced for the first time to kill fleas and lice.

Chapter 5

Maelor General Hospital

Following the closure of the Emergency Military Services Hospital, the old Plas Maelor re-opened as the Maelor General Hospital, sharing the medical and surgical care of the local population with the War Memorial Hospital. All surgical, medical and gynaecological cases were transferred from Croesnewydd Infirmary to the Maelor Hospital, which also accommodated clinics. Croesnewydd Infirmary continued to care for the maternity and the elderly chronic sick cases. Extra medical staff were employed — doctors, nurses, pathologist, radiographers and physiotherapists as well as ancillaries — kitchen and dining room staff, cleaners and porters. Matron Nellie Parry continued to be in charge of Croesnewydd Infirmary and her duties were expanded to cover the new Maelor Hospital with Miss Sarah Williams as her deputy. When the National Health Act came into force, the Maelor General Hospital, came under the Ministry of Health.

This, however, meant that there was no establishment to care for the elderly in the area and, under the terms of the National Assistance Act all local authorities were required to provide, amongst other things, help and accommodation for those in need. Gladwyn Hall in Gresford, was acquired and opened on the 15 August 1948 to provide accommodation for 30 elderly residents of both sexes. This was a 'feather in Denbighshire County Council's hat' as it was the first such home in Wales. These improved circumstances, enabled those folk who had been transferred to Forden and Welshpool, at the beginning of the war, to come back to their own area. As finances became available, other homes were established, thirteen of which were in existence at the time of the amalgamation of Denbighshire and Flintshire to form the County of Clwyd. These homes were: Acrefair, near Wrexham; Erddig, near Wrexham; Gladwyn, Gresford; Awelon, Ruthin; Argoed Hall, Froncysyllte; Greenacres, Wrexham; Awel-y-Mor, Abergele; New Hall, Ruabon; Bod Euryn, Colwyn Bay; Pen-y-Nant, Minera; Bryn Derwen, Llanrwst; Wren's Nest, Wrexham; Dolwen, Denbigh.

Most of the trained nursing staff at the Maelor General Hospital, were local, having trained in Liverpool or Chester Hospitals and quite a few State Enrolled Nurses came from Croesnewydd Hospital where they had been trained. The Maelor General Hospital was not, at this time, a nurse training school.

Uniform

Sisters wore a long-sleeved, navy-blue dress with white cuffs and collar, a navy belt and a small white, frilled cap.

Staff Nurses wore in green dresses with white collars, short sleeves and white ruffles, a green belt and a small, white cap.

Charge Nurses wore a white coat with navy epaulettes.

State Enrolled Nurses wore green/white striped short-sleeved dresses with white collars and white ruffles, a striped belt and a small, white cap.

Nursing Auxiliaries wore a mid-blue short-sleeved dress (with collar and belt the same colour) and a small, white cap. Their white aprons had long tapes which crossed at the back and fastened into the belt of the apron. There were as many as seven or eight Nursing Auxiliaries per ward, graded according to seniority, once they had proved efficient in carrying out their tasks. This was valuable experience for a young woman and many went on to train and become State Registered Nurses at other training hospitals.

Porters

The porters were based in the entrance hall and were responsible for the Maelor Hospital side. They wore brown smocks and a brown, hard cap. The head porter, Mr Large, was based in a room at the enquiry office, which was manned by other duty porters, in the building on the right-hand side of the entry gates, opposite the pathology department. They also carried out work for Croesnewydd Hospital.

When removing a dead person from the ward to the mortuary , the procedure was always carried out in a very dignified and compassionate manner and it was always the custom for the porters to remove their hats.

Male surgical ward, Maelor General Hospital. On the left, a doctor, accompanied by a sister, carries out a ward round. In the far corner, SEN Bill Whittingham explains a procedure to a student. On the right, a student nurse takes observations on a patient.

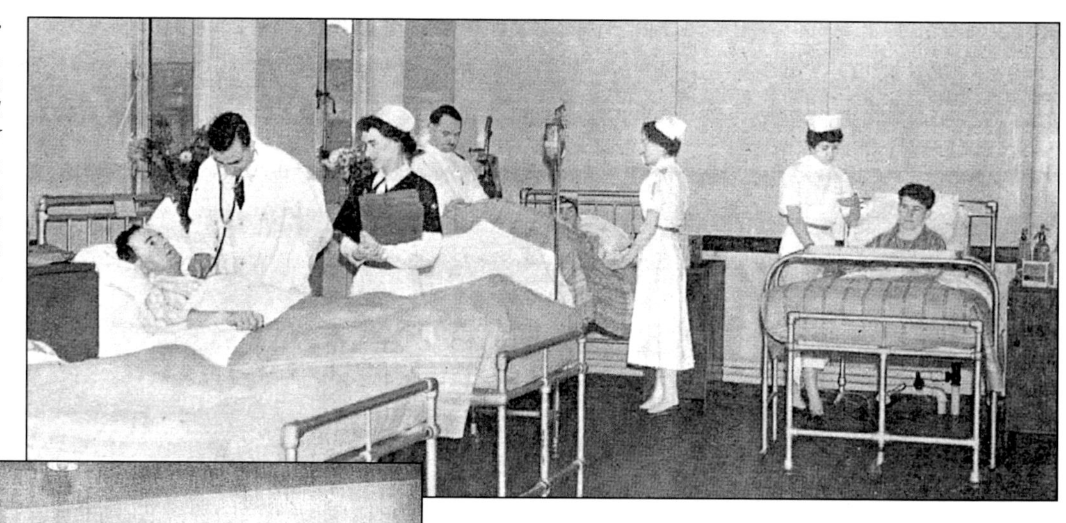

Nurses' sitting room at the Maelor General Hospital in the early 1960s.

Charge nurse John Dickens poses for a photograph with staff and a patient on the male surgical ward at the Maelor Hospital.

Above: Gardeners at work at the Maelor General Hospital.

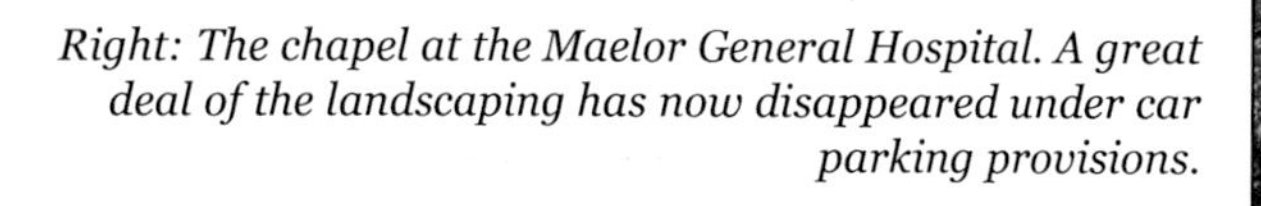

Right: The chapel at the Maelor General Hospital. A great deal of the landscaping has now disappeared under car parking provisions.

Prize Day, Maelor Nurses Training School, 1957. Guest of Honour Mr Robert S. Ninian sitting next to Matron Margaret Hammond and Asst Matron Miss Sarah Williams. Note the military style capes worn by the two nurse administrators,Miss Mitchel and Miss W. Jones.

Ward Maids (Domestics)

Theses ladies had a great deal of influence on the wards, and ruled their areas with a rod of iron. If any talcum powder or water was spilled on the floor, the culprit was sought out by the ward maid making junior nurses nervous wrecks. Cleaning was meticulously carried out by these people, everywhere was spotlessly clean and shining— their ward was their pride and joy.

Break and lunch times

Nurses operated a rota system for their break and lunch. They went to the dining room where everyone sat at their specified tables, according to their grade, four people to a table. The tables were always covered by snow-white table cloths, with a water carafe and glasses. There was waitress service, the waitresses wearing black dresses with small, frilled aprons and white, frilled hats. The doctors had a separate dining room, run by different staff.

Head Cook and Assistants

Head cooks wore white dresses with aprons and high, white caps. Kitchen assistants wore a greyish coloured dress and white aprons and hats. Male assistants wore greyish cotton trousers and a short white coat and hat. At this time rationing was still in progress and wards were allocated tea, butter and sugar, according to patient numbers and their rations. A patient's ration book had to be produced by a relative. Sister Winnie Jones was the senior sister in charge of the kitchen and she inspected all ward kitchens for cleanliness and kept an eye on the patients' rations.

At the hospital's Christmas lunch, the cook, who was a large lady, and her assistant, always came in after the main course carrying a large 'brandy flamed' Christmas pudding.

Physiotherapy Department

Physiotherapy is an important part of health care and, over the years, there have been many physiotherapists employed at the War Memorial Hospital, Croesnewydd Hospital and the Maelor general Hospital. In the early days a Miss Egan was in charge of the department and she was succeeded by Miss Enid Griffiths. Miss Sybil Edwards joined the department during the 1940s as did Miss Joyce Dudley. In the mid 1940s Mr Jim Wilson took charge of the department. There were also two physiotherapy aides who worked in the department for many years: Miss Doris Davies and Miss Phylis Hatton. The senior physiotherapist was Mr Pratt who worked at the Croesnewydd and Maelor hospitals for many years. He spent a great deal of time working in the isolation unit where physiotherapy could be quite demanding, especially for those patients in the iron lungs. Physiotherapists could be state registered or chartered.

Male physiotherapists wore a long white coat, navy trousers and a white shirt. In the early days, female physiotherapists wore a long white coat, navy skirts and white blouses, with a fine cotton hat which was folded and pinned to the back of the head with a point hanging at the back. Later, females were allowed to wear a short white jacket, navy skirt or trousers and small pill-box hats. The hats were eventually discarded.

One of the physios, Miss Joyce Dudley, was rather special. As a teenager she had lost the sight in her right eye whilst still a pupil at Grove Park School. On completing her formal education in 1936, she applied, and was accepted, to do nurse training at the Robert Jones & Agnes Hunt Orthopaedic Hospital, Gobowen, with the aim of eventually becoming a physiotherapist. Six months into her training she lost the sight in her other eye, rendering her completely blind. Unable to continue with her training she was obliged to leave but, much against her parent's wishes, still hankered to become a physiotherapist. She eventually heard about Great Portland Street Hospital in London which ran a training course for blind physiotherapists. She applied and was accepted for a month's probationary period and then, in July 1939, began the full training course. She qualified in 1941 and commenced work at the EMS Hospital in Wrexham in January 1942. She worked at the Maelor General Hospital and the War Memorial Hospital for many years, retiring in March 1980. In June of that year she was awarded the MBE.

Nurse training

In 1956 the Maelor General Hospital was approved by the Nursing Council for England and Wales to become a nurse training school called the Wrexham School of Nursing. The Maelor students, together with the War Memorial students, attended Strathalyn Preliminary Training School for nurses at Rossett. After successfully completing this course they were then accepted for training either at the War Memorial Hospital or the Maelor General Hospital.

Lectures and general studies were taken in the teaching department at the War Memorial. Nurses were seconded from the War Memorial Hospital to the Maelor to gain experience on the children's wards and in gynaecology whilst Maelor students went to the War Memorial for experience in orthopaedics, casualty, ENT and eye nursing. In about 1963, a general integration of students began to take place and they were allocated to wards and departments in both hospitals.

The Maelor Hospital nurses' wore a military style uniform:

1st year student — white dress, with pink epaulettes and belt, and white cap.
2nd year student — white dress, with pink and brown epaulettes and belt, and white cap.
3rd year student — white dress with brown epaulettes and belt, and white cap.
When the students passed their hospital final examinations they had a pale blue stripe added to their brown epaulettes and belt, and white cap.
Enrolled Nurses — wore a white dress of a finer material than the students, with buttons down either side, so that it could be flapped over to a cleaner side, with green epaulettes and belt and small, white cap.
Staff Nurse —- had a white dress in a finer, more silky material, which had buttons down both sides, so that it could be flapped over for a cleaner side. They had navy-blue epaulettes, a belt and a white cap.
Sisters — had a white, long-sleeved dress, with a short navy-blue military type cape, and a white cap with lace edging.
Nurse Administration — wore a white dress, with a maroon short cape and belt, and a small, white laced cap.
Matron – wore a navy dress of a fine material, with small, white laced collar and cuffs and a white laced hat. At a later date wore a pale grey dress, with white laced collar and cuffs, and a white frilled cap.

In the late 1960s Matron Bridger changed the Maelor nurses' uniform, to become the same as that worn in the War Memorial Hospital.

Pathology

The first hospital pathology department was set up at the War Memorial Hospital where it was situated on the first floor of the private patients wing (part of the old William & John Jones Hospital). Between the 1930s and 1950s the chief technician was Mr Ted Ellis. As the volume of path lab work increased more space was required and, in the late 1950s it was moved to a building located outside, between the x-ray department and the main kitchen, access being through a door off the main corridor.

During the 1940s junior porters from the War Memorial Hospital collected specimens from the Maelor and Croesnewydd hospitals, on carrier bicycles, for the War Memorial pathology laboratory and returned the results when ready.

In the mid to late 1950s, the Maelor Hospital pathology department was itself developing and the War Memorial laboratory concentrated on blood transfusions and other work, while the Maelor laboratory concentrated on haematology and other specialties. The porters continued to provide the delivery and collection system but now for both hospital sites, the bicycles being eventually replaced by vans.

A rather indistinct press photograph of pathologist Dr Lionel Wise, inspecting a new blood testing machine, March 1972

Tom Crossley, senior laboratory technician, retires. A group of laboratory staff pose for a photograph and wish him a 'Happy Retirement'. [Gareth Davies]
Back row L–R: Tony Coates, Margaret Ankers, Helen Harding, Melanie Williams, Dave Howell, Janet Roberts, Caroline Owens, Peter Karan, John Phillips, Marie Walker, Siân Evans, Debie Taylor, Yvonne Wright, John Armitage, Peter Derek 3rd Row: Gareth Davies, Eldred Ankers, Gilbert Roberts, Garry Dean, Brett Roberts, Alwyn Lloyd, Kevin Holland, Alexis Batty, Many Challoner, Pat Crewe, Gerald Thomas, Mike Smith, Rob Jones, Martyn Davies, Teresa Mathews. 2nd Row: Norma Johnson, Jill Mitchell, Jude Leslie, Lidia Jenkins, Veronica Bugh, Sian Mayberry, Pat Kinsella, Evelyn Hasty, Pat Ryan, Jamie Taylor, Peter Howell, Irene Lewis. Front Row: Pauline Davies, Helen Jones, Shirley Tudor, Helen Pugh, Roger Dodman, Tom Crossley, T. P. Rollason, D. K. Watson, C. P. Williams, Malcolm Seller, R. H. P. Reid, R. B. Williams.

Maelor General Hospital Pharmacy staff, 1989.

The laboratory technicians from the War Memorial and the Maelor worked an on-call system between them to provide cover for nights and weekends.

In 1966 a new cytology department was set up within the Maelor pathology department and, in about 1970, the pathology department at the War Memorial Hospital closed and all work was carried out at the Maelor Hospital.

Pharmacy

This was originally located in the outpatients department and was staffed by two pharmacists, and a technician. Gradually, after the introduction of the NHS, the volume of work increased and the pharmacy was moved to a detached building (shared with other services such as the medical secretaries, social workers, the hearing aid department and the sewing room) close to the outpatients department. Until the 1960s strict economy was practiced, and then the disposable age came in with a 'bang'. A complete transformation then occurred in nursing, with disposable syringes, needles, paper towels (instead of cotton), surgeons gloves, catheters, incontinent sheets, etc. Hygienically a tremendous step forward, but financially, costs soared. New drugs seemed to be introduced almost on a daily basis.

A new department was built at the Maelor General Hospital in the 1960s which also served the War Memorial Hospital. Mr Ralph Davies was the Chief Administrator of Pharmaceuticals until 1989.

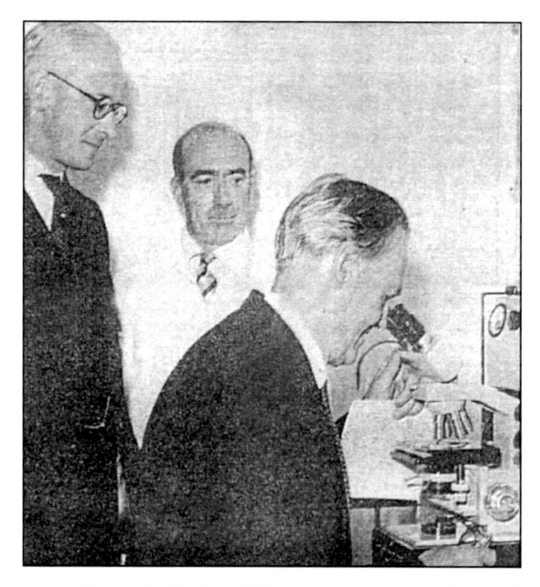

*Above L–R: Lord Kenyon, Tom Crossley and Charles Loughlin (Under Sec. to the Minister of Health) at the opening of the new cytology unit, Maelor Hospital, July 1966. [*Wrexham Gazette*]*

Surgical Services

The following is an excerpt from *Newyddion Maelor News* 1998, written by clinical director and consultant surgeon Mr Mick Crumplin

> When I arrived at the Maelor in the autumn of 1977, I realised that I was only the sixth consultant surgeon to be appointed at this hospital. Up to the 1950s, a lot of the surgery at both the Maelor and the War Memorial was under-taken by general practitioner surgeons, and visiting consultants from centres of eminence.
>
> On arriving at Wrexham I realised the population that we had, derived mainly from an industrial and agricultural society, and the work offered by this population was plentiful and often a great challenge. All four, consultant surgeons undertook urology, the workload of this speciality taking up between 20% and 30% of the work we performed. Mr Ron Todd and Mr Jack Laine undertook an interest in vascular and upper gastro intestinal specialities respectively, and Mr Laurence Tinkler had undertaken a speciality interest in urology. I was appointed as a general surgeon with an upper gastro intestinal interest. We all performed minor straightforward paediatric surgery.
>
> The need for increased specialisation among surgeons, within district general hospitals was seen to be inevitable as patients were demanding to see surgeons with expertise in their particular complaint. The problem we had to come to terms with was that such specialists also needed to be general surgeons as well, when they were on emergency take-in, they would have to deal safely with every surgical condition presented through the doors of the emergency admission ward or casualty.
>
> The Division of Surgery has traditionally provided a good deal of input into various levels of examination in Edinburgh and English Royal College of Surgeons. Mr Todd, Mr Pye and myself have all been examiners elected for the Royal College of England for the FRCS, and Mr Laine has been elected as an examiner for the Royal College of Surgeons of Edinburgh. I was fortunate to have been Chairman of the Court of Examiners, for two years at the Royal College of Surgeons of England. Wrexham Maelor Hospital is only the second hospital ever in Wales to have hosted the Fellowship examination, which it did first in 1997. This was organised by Mr Pye.
>
> Quality of service must be our byword for the next 50 years, with increasing specialisation (but retention of generalist abilities) good rapport with patients, and safe surgery the key issues for the Division of Surgery.

Mr Tinkler.

Staff and patients on the Hans Anderson children's ward, Maelor General Hospital, 1950s.

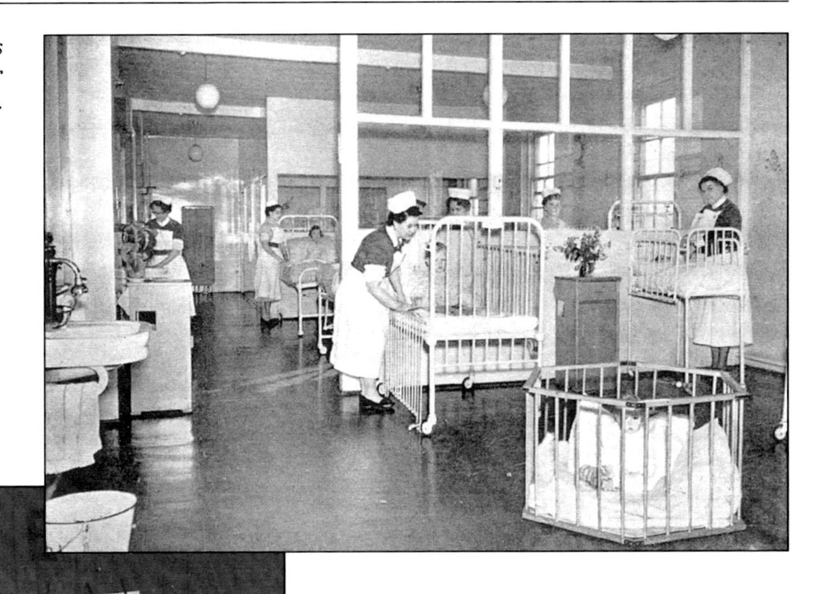

Staff 'Olde Tyme' variety show, Maelor General Hospital, 1970s.

Retirement of Kathleen Hughes, doctor's 'house mother', 1990.

Mr Wally Meredith, the chief electronics engineer, and his staff, provided a vital support role to every department in the hospital.

Maelor General Hospital medical Staff, 1984.
Front row L–R: Dr M. M. C. Gilchrist, Dr E. G. G. Roberts, Mr J. B. Laine, Dr J. T. Baker, Dr M. G. E. Greensmith, Dr W. J. W. Thomas, Mr T. E. Jeffreys, Mr R. S. Todd, Dr A. Ross, Dr R. Williams.
Middle row: Dr V. Jones, Mr M. K. H. Crumplin, Dr D. T. Jones, Dr D. F. Child, Mr P. R. Vlies, Dr C. A. Wadon, Dr C. H. Stephenson.
Back row: Dr A. E. Edwards, Mr J. G. Heyes, Dr J. A. Craig, Mr J. D. Hamlett, Mr M. A. T. Cook, Dr D. Allen, Dr T. P. Rollason.
[Ysbyty Maelor Trust Board]

Maelor General Hospital, c.1980. This building was used as the general offices and, later, for mental health care.

Sterilisation

In the early days of the War Memorial Hospital the sterilisation of ward dressing drums was carried out by the general theatre which was in possession of a large autoclave machine known, because of the noise and steam which it produced, as 'Billy'. Each ward drum contained dressings, dressing towels and surgical gloves. The autoclave was operated by a nurse. In the 1960s a sterilisation unit was established at the rear of the nurses' home at Plas yn Llwyn under the supervision of Sister Thomas. The introduction of disposal dressings and equipment greatly lightened the load on the sterilisation department and on the nursing staff in general; only theatres continued to sterilise their own materials. In 1976 Sister Thomas retired and was succeeded by Mr John Garsden as general manager and he introduced the Theatre Sterile Support Unit which meant that all departments were now serviced by the sterilisation unit. In 1991, a purpose-built Hospital Sterile Disinfectant Unit was built close to the Maelor General Hospital which later became known as the Central Sterilisation Support Department.

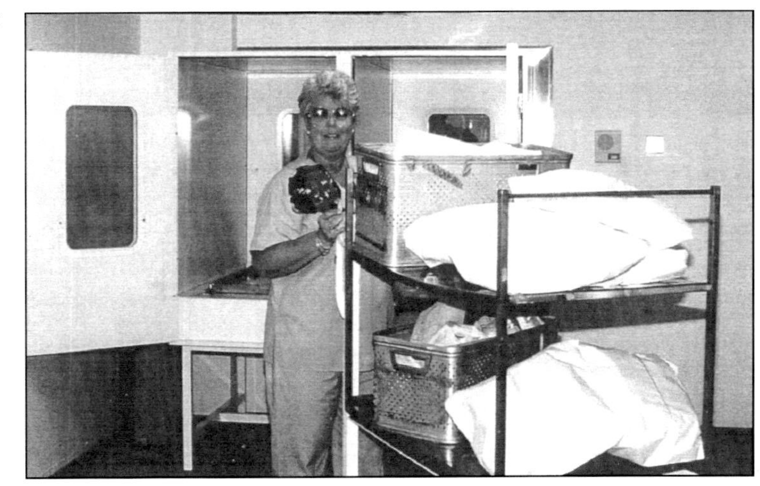

All hospitals in the Wrexham area used the Maelor's department. In this photograph prepared packs are about to be placed in the autoclave sterilisation machine.

Chapter 6

The Dispensary & Wrexham Infirmary

Medical care in the nineteenth century

Medical care was very limited during this period. Doctors (medical practitioners) were available but their treatment was limited and the poorer section of the community could not afford their fees and, as a result, many turned to the village 'quack' or 'old wife' for help and would be given herbal remedies and other advice on how to treat their ailments, at an affordable rate.

By the early 1800s drugists (pharmacutical chemists) and apothecaries were available in Wrexham High Street. The druggist was a recognised supplier of medicine while an apothecary tended to encroach on the rôle of the doctor and carried out his own diagnosis and prescribing.

The Wrexham Dispensary

The Wrexham Dispensary was opened in Yorke Street, on the 1 May 1833, as a result of the efforts of Dr Taylor Griffith (1795–1876) a prominent local physician, with the encouragement of Sir Watkin Williams Wynn. The year before the Dispensary was opened, Dr Griffith had the honour of attending the young Princess Victoria when she was taken ill whilst staying at the Wynnstay Hall, Ruabon. Dr Griffith was the son of a Wrexham practitioner and an ex-pupil of the Wrexham Grammar School. He was the founder of the north Wales branch of the British Medical Association.

Dr Thomas Taylor Griffith. [WAWC]

The Dispensary had no facilities for in-patients and during the first two years more than 1,700 poor people were treated as out-patients. According to the rules, an annual subscription of £1 would cover one patient's treatment and the benefits were restricted to: mechanics and labourerers (and their wives and children), servants (whose wages did not exceed £3 a year), poor persons not able to pay for medical advice in the usual way and those not receiving parish relief. There was also a subscription scheme of 1d (less that

Yorke Street photographed in the 1930s. The view of the street had changed little since the 19th century. The Dispensary was located on the right-hand side near the top of the street, next door to the Wynnstay Vaults. [WAWC]

.5p) a week, whereby a man and his family could benefit. Medicine was provided from stock. Patients could select from a list of doctors and be attended at home if living within a mile of the Dispensary, with a sliding charge for those living further away.

Patients had to furnish clean bottles for medicines, and galli pots (small earthenware pots) for ointments etc. while all bandages supplied by the Dispensary had to be returned clean when done with. No female in labour could be attended, but she was entitled to medical attendance after childbirth, during the post-natal period.

As a result of the generous support of the public, the Dispensary provided valuable services to the poor and its benevolent work grew so quickly that, in a year or two, it became obvious that there was the need to erect a new building which would combine the services of the dispensary with those of an infirmary. A fund was opened and £300 was set aside from the Yorke Street Dispensary, and put towards this fund. A three day bazaar was held in the Town Hall during Wrexham Race Week, which raised £1,053-8s.-3d. and by the end of 1837, the project had taken shape, and the subscribers were able to see the plans drawn up for the building of the new infirmary.

The Wrexham Infirmary 1838–1926

The Wrexham Infirmary was opened in 1838 in Regent Street and a stylish stone portico was added to the front of the building, a gift from Dr Taylor Griffith.

The honorary surgeon was Dr Parker, who was also the first consultant physician. Other doctors who worked at the Infirmary were: Dr T. T. Griffith, Dr Hugh Hughes, Dr George Lewis and Dr V. P. Royton. Mr R. M. Lloyd became treasurer, and Mr D. Thomas acted as dispenser and hospital secretary. Many benefactors pledged either an annual or one-off subscriptions to support the establishment. Initially, only out-patients were treated.

In 1840 the supporters of the Infirmary launched another fund raising campaign to build sick wards which could accommodate in-patients in the new establishment. This first ward would accommodate four patients and was called Victoria Ward, after the Queen who had recently acceded to the throne.

When in-patients began to be accepted, a matron and extra nurses were appointed. According to the rules of the establishment, the matron had to be between the age of 30 and 50, and, in addition to her nursing duties, had to do all the cooking. The nurses had to clean their wards daily, and give them an extra clean and scrubbing once a week. Once the patients were up and about, the matron set to work all those who she deemed to be capable — helping with the washing, the ironing of light articles and any other work she thought they would be capable of doing, except kitchen duty.

In the early days, patients had to provide their own bed linen and medicine bottles, and return all bandages to the dispensary in a spotlessly clean state after use.

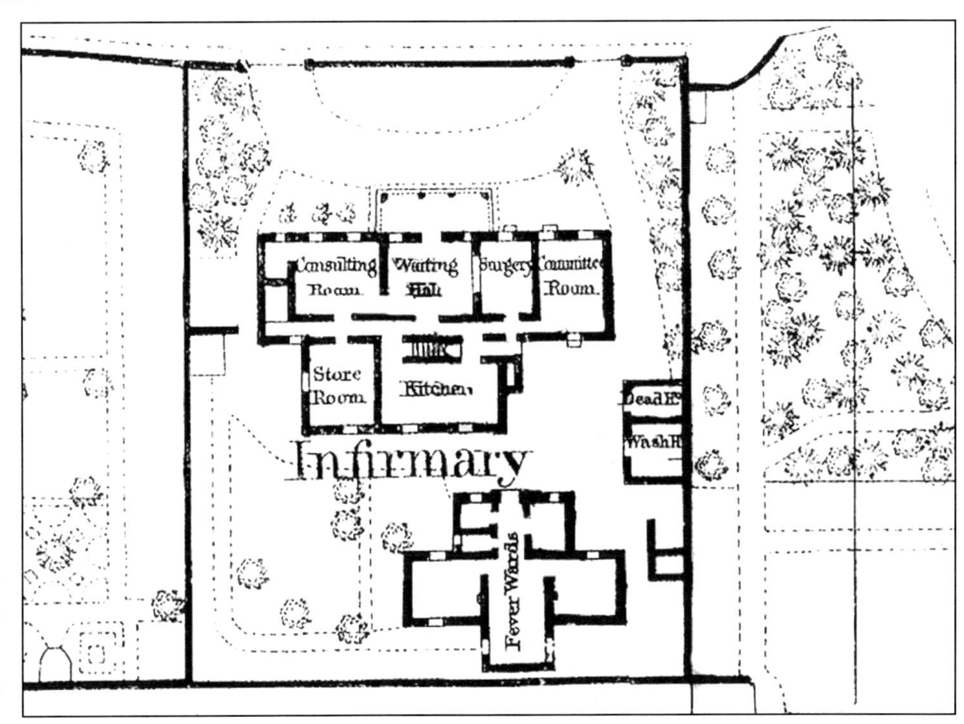

The ground floor layout of the original Infirmary in 1872. Regent Street is at the top of the drawing and the sketched in outline of Bradley Road on the right. [DRO]

Wrexham Infirmary as it was built in 1838.

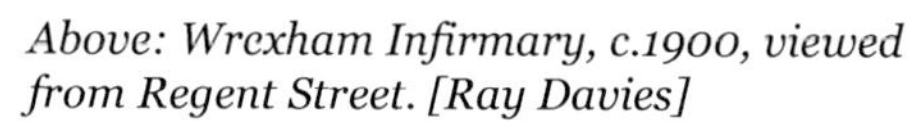

Above: Wrexham Infirmary, c.1900, viewed from Regent Street. [Ray Davies]

Left: Wrexham Infirmary, c.1900, viewed from Caxton Place with St Mary's RC Cathedral and St Mark's Church in the background. [Ray Davies]

A second ward was opened the following year, and by 1844, 12,000 patients had received treatment at the Infirmary.

In 1847, Dr John Dickenson administered the first general anaesthetic at the Infirmary to a patient who had a successful limb amputation, certainly the first general anaesthetic to be administered in north Wales, and quite possibly in the whole of Wales. Dr Dickenson was a strong advocate of improvements to the drainage and water supplies of the district, and became Mayor of Wrexham in 1861.

Dr John Dickenson [WAWC]

By 1860, the Infirmary was dealing with over 2,000 patients each year and in 1863 a new operating theatre and drug room were built, funded by public subscriptions. Three years later, Wrexham businessman, William Overton financed new fever wards which were built at the rear of the main building (which can be seen on the 1872 OS map). In 1881 Mr Oswald Bury became the hospital secretary and, during his term of office, the fever wards were closed and converted into a large dispensary and out-patients department. By 1887, the institution was running into financial difficulties which was resolved by yet another public subscription which also provided a new children's ward and a convalescent ward (at a cost of £910).

1890 saw the beginning of organised subscriptions by workmen via their place of work. In 1889 the 12-bed Piercy Ward (named after benefactor Benjamin Piercy) was opened along with the Piercy Nursing Institution which was accommodated in Hope Villa, next door to the Infirmary. The Overton block (paid for by a bequest from Mrs Overton), consisting of two 10-bed wards, was erected in 1902 as were King Edward VII Ward (male) and Queen Alexandra Ward (female) which were opened by Mrs Soames of Bryn Estyn.

The 1906 salary reports show the monthly costs of the staff:

Dr Thorley (house surgeon)	£6-13s.-4d.	Matron	£5-8s.-4d.
Dispenser	£2-18s.-4d.	Nurse	£2-10s.-0d.
Asst. nurse	£1-15s.-0d.	Other helpers	£1-10s.-0d.
Cook	£2-2s.-2d.	House maid	£1-6s.-8d.
Ward maid	£1-5s.-0d.	Nurses home maid	£ 19s.-2d.
Kitchen maid	£ 16s.-8d.		

To keep the overheads as low as possible, the Infirmary kept its own pigs and poultry. By 1911, the organised workmen's subscriptions were bringing in over £900 each year and by 1923 this had risen to £5,878-10s.-8d.

In 1916, a committee was convened to look at the possibility of building new wards but it was unanimously agreed that what was needed was a new hospital. Ironically, having made the decision in 1918 to build what became the War Memorial Hospital, the Wrexham Infirmary received a royal visit from King George V, Queen Mary and Princess Mary on 16 July 1920.

In 1922, the Infirmary received a gift of money from the Wrexham branch of the War Supply Depot, Queen Mary's Needlework Guild and the Cefn & District Co-operative Society which was utilised to buy the town's first motorised ambulance which was handed over on 12 January.

A Morton Inhaler.
The picture shows a Morton's Inhaler similar to the one used by Dr Dickenson in 1847. Note the sponge in the glass container, which would have been soaked in ether solution. When the patient inhaled through the connecting tube, the gasses from the ether soaked sponge would anaesthetise the patient. The Morton Inhaler was first mentioned in the North Wales Chronicle *on 22 December 1846. It was named after a surgeon in Boston (USA) who invented it. The ether that they used was called 'Letheon' and it was used mainly in dentistry. The adverse effects that were recognised were of vomiting and so an empty stomach was advocated prior to anaesthesia. The dangers were that ether was highly inflammable and precautions had to be taken. A report was issued on the successful administration of anaesthetic to a patient by Dr Dickenson in the* Carnarvon & Denbigh Herald, *and the* North Wales Chronicle *in February 1847.*

Views of two almost identical views of wards at Wrexham Infirmary which were both opened in 1902.

Left: King Edward VII Ward (male).

Below: Queen Alexandra Ward (female).

Wrexham Infirmary staff pose for a photograph in the hospital gardens on Regent Street, early 1900s.

The Infirmary's first motor ambulance, manufactured by the Belgian Minerva company, parked outside the main door. Seated in the front is Mr Spencer, clerk to the hospital.

Chapter 7

The War Memorial Hospital

Known locally as the 'War Memorial Hospital' this institution is, in fact, two hospitals — the Wrexham & East Denbighshire Memorial Hospital and the William & John Jones Hospital — which developed simultaneously alongside each other on land surrounding the house known as 'Roseneath' that had been part of the bequest of John Jones.

Roseneath (1914–8)

In 1864, William Low, the noted engineer, built a house on part of the former Grove Park estate, which he called 'Roseneath'. He was a self-made Victorian industrialist, involved in the building of tunnels (he proposed and made a start on building a Channel tunnel under the Straits of Dover), railways and mining. In 1912, the house was bought by John Jones with the specific intention of it being converted into a hospital under the control of the William & John Jones Hospital Trust. John, along with his brother William (who had died in 1904), had founded the Island Green Brewery, and was a generous benefactor of the Wrexham area. He lived in Grove Lodge, on the corner of Grove Road and Chester Road.

Before any use could be made of Roseneath as a hospital, the First World War broke out and the house was taken over as a military hospital, run by military personnel, doctors, nurses (including Red Cross nurses and VADs) with a matron in charge. Doctor Enoch Moss was the non-military surgeon/physician. Most of the soldiers treated here were convalescing.

An elderly lady, Mrs J. L. Percival from Ellesmere Port, recalled that military casualties were heavy during this time,

Wrexham benefactor John Jones and Roseneath, the house built by William Low in 1864, which formed a substantial part of the William & John Jones Hospital Trust. [WAWC]

Various photographs of wounded and disabled soldiers, nurses and civilian and military medical staff at Roseneath during the First World War. The soldiers are wearing 'hospital blues', a light-blue uniform with a red tie, issued to soldiers whilst in hospital. Those in caps are wearing their regulation khaki service caps with distinguishing regimental or corps cap badge. [DRO]

Above: A wounded soldier relaxing in the garden at Roseneath in a wicker perambulator. [DRO]

Above: The doctor second from the left in this photograph is Dr Moss. [DRO]

Above and right: Wounded soldiers, nursing staff and members of the public indulge in a game of quoits on the lawns at Roseneath. The slope on the right led up to the front door of the house. [DRO]

and that they arrived in their blood stained uniforms at Wrexham Railway Station at all hours of the day or night, and were taken to Roseneath. She stated that many women from the Wrexham area became VADs and gave hours of devoted service to the hospital. Her mother, who lived locally, was a VAD and was often called out when a hospital train was expected. Mrs Percival, who worked at Hoole Hospital, spent many hours of her hospital leave helping at Roseneath.

The Wrexham & East Denbighshire Memorial Hospital

Following a public meeting held in the summer of 1918, plans were announced to build a new hospital in conjunction with the William & John Jones Hospital Trust as a memorial to the men of Wrexham and east Denbighshire who had been killed in the First World War. The initial cost was estimated to be £100,000 of which £50,000 would be provided by the Trust.

On 2 November 1923, HRH The Prince of Wales visited Wrexham to lay the foundation stone of the new hospital. Sometime after 4pm, to the peal of the Parish Church bells and the boom of the detonators on the railway, the prince arrived at Wrexham General. His fist stop was at the Parciau where he received an enthusiastic welcome from the hundreds of children in attendance, and met a number of local dignitaries on the band stand. After a brief inspection of the Royal Welch Fusiliers who were mounting a guard of honour at the junction of Ruthin Road and Bradley Road he made his way to the site of the new hospital where he alighted from his car at the junction of Grosvenor Road and Rhosddu Road and proceeded on foot through another guard of honour made up of ex-service men, Girl Guides and Boy Scouts, into the hospital grounds. There he made his way to a raised platform, through yet another guard of honour, this time made up of nurses from the Wrexham Infirmary and the Fever Hospital, and the local VAD nurses. After a few speeches the prince carried out the stone-laying ceremony using a silver trowel and a silver mounted oak mallet. The stone was inscribed: 'This stone was laid by HRH The Prince of Wales, KG, November 2nd 1923'.

The original artist's impression of what the War Memorial Hospital could have looked like. As it was, several of the buildings seen here, along with the tower on the main block, were never built.

HRH Prince Henry (later the Duke of Gloucester) performs the official opening of the Wrexham & East Denbighshire Memorial Hospital. [DRO]

Wrexham & East Denbighshire Memorial Hospital.

Wrexham & East Denbighshire Memorial Hospital. The wing on the right of the photograph was the Prince of Wales Ward (ground floor) with Overton Ward above. The second floor was added to this wing shortly before the Second World War, following a donation of £10,000 by Mrs Evington. Note the round structures on either side of the wing, which housed the ward bathrooms and toilets on one side, with the sluices on the other side.

The main entrance hall to the new hospital. The door to the left of the main doorway later led to the hospital telephone exchange and the door on the right led to the matron's office. The plaques high up on the wall recorded, bilingually 'Memorial Hospital. Built in memory of the brave men of Wrexham and East Denbighshire, 1914–1918/ Ysbyty Goffa. Adeiladwyd er cof am ddewrion Gwercsam a dwyrain Sir Ddinbych'. [DRO]

The Pantomime Ward, clearly showing the light, airy nature of the new facilities. [DRO]

One of the upstairs corridors. [DRO]

The kitchen at the new hospital. [DRO]

On 9 June 1926 HRH Prince Henry paid a special visit to Wrexham to formally open the Wrexham & East Denbighshire Memorial Hospital, and the William & John Jones Hospital (the former was always known locally as the War Memorial Hospital, a name which later also encompassed the William & John Jones Hospital). The new building, which had been erected and equipped at a cost of over £84,000, could accommodate 103 patients and replaced the Wrexham Infirmary, which had beds for only 54 patients. The honorary surgeons, house surgeon, nursing and other staff were now able to carry out their work in an establishment that was deemed to be second to none.

In design, appliances and equipment no effort was spared to bring the hospital up to the standards of the latest developments in medical science in an area with a population of 100,000. There were special male and female wards, while others catered for eye cases, medical and surgical patients. Each ward accommodated fourteen patients. There was also an x-ray department, pathology laboratory, vaccine rooms and an up-to-date operating theatre with ante rooms, anaesthetic and recovery rooms. There was a large massage room (physiotherapy) and a large, well-equipped laundry. A separate wing accommodated ten private patients.

The hospital's main entrance, on Rhosddu Road, opened onto a large reception hall, around which were located examination rooms with bathrooms, clothes fumigator, storage and the offices of the matron, the medical officer, the hospital secretary and the clerks. These examination rooms and bathrooms were later altered into offices for Matron Heeley, the deputy matron, the hospital secretary (Mr Lesley Spencer), the matron's secretary, clerks and the hospital switchboard. The floor of the reception hall was covered in marble, with a distinctive coloured mosaic design which extended into the ground floor corridor leading to the various wards and departments, including out-patients. A few yards along the main corridor from reception, on the left hand side, was Pantomime Ward and, on the right, Prince of Wales Ward. Pantomime Ward was named after the Walter Roberts Pantomime Company which was a regular benefactor to medical care in the local community, originally to the Wrexham Infirmary and then the War Memorial Hospital. The company performed pantomimes annually and the proceeds from these events paid for each individual bed on Pantomime Ward. Prince of Wales Ward was, of course, named after Prince Edward who laid the hospital's foundation stone. These wards accommodated fourteen patients, but, in emergencies such as serious pit accidents, camp beds were set up in the middle of the wards. At the end of each ward were, on the one side, toilets and and bathroom, and on the other side, the sluice room. Each large ward had a single-bedded ward, with its own bathroom and toilet and, opposite, there was a two-bedded ward with the same amenities. These side wards often held patients who required specialist care. There was also the sister's office, the staff changing room, the ward kitchen, linen room and sterilising room.

Off the main corridor, on the Pantomime Ward side, there were stairs on the right which led down to the basement and up to the first floor. There was also a lift which went to the top floor.

Overton Ward was on the right-hand side of the first floor, above the Prince of Wales Ward, and the Cunliffe Ward was on the left above the Pantomime Ward. All wards were of the same design.

On the first floor, at the top of the stairs, were large double doors on the opposite side of the corridor, which led to

War Memorial Hospital medical and nursing staff with members of the management board, 1920s. Seated in the centre of the front row is Matron Heeley; two to her left is Dr Glyn Evans and two to her right is Dr Enoch Moss. The photograph is taken outside the arcade at the William & John Jones Hospital, in front of what later became Morris Ward.

The Elms, on Rhosddu Road was originally built as a private house and was once the home of the Croom-Johnson family and later, the home of Richard Geoffrey Williams, a prominent physician and surgeon. It was sold to the War Memorial Hospital in 1939 and served as a home for the junior doctors and later, nurses. Today, it is the premises of the mental health department. [WAWC]

The operating theatre at the War Memorial Hospital. [DRO]

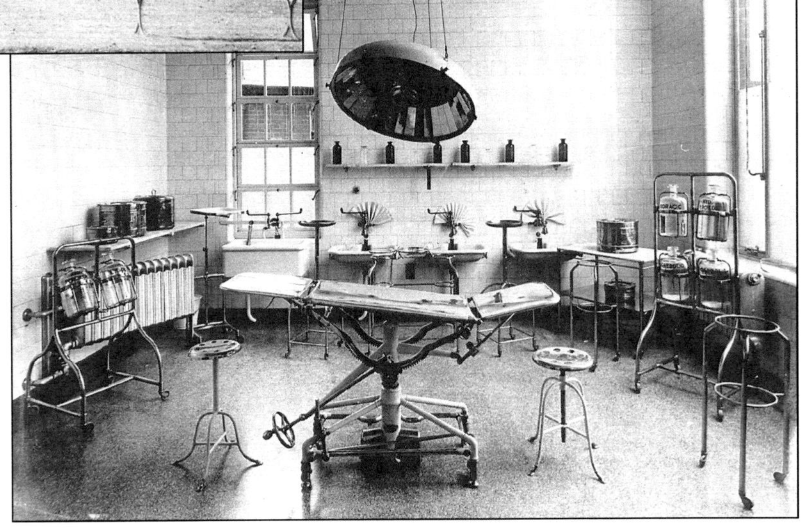

Wrexham & E.D. War Memorial Hospital.

Goodwill this Xmas.

IT COSTS

£33,000 to keep the Hospital for 1 Year.
1/3d. ,, ,, ,, ,, 1 Minute

WILL YOU KEEP THE HOSPITAL FOR A FEW MINUTES ?

THE 1941 XMAS APPEAL RAISED £172/15/0.
To ALL DONORS—THANK YOU.

Please pass this Envelope round your Table.
REMEMBER YOUR HOSPITAL THIS

CHRISTMAS.

£ Pennies make Pounds. £

To Save Paper and Labour, no Letter enclosed.

Name...

Address...

NOTE.—Street Collections are strictly forbidden.

Fund raising envelope, 1942. [Mr E.Jeffreys]

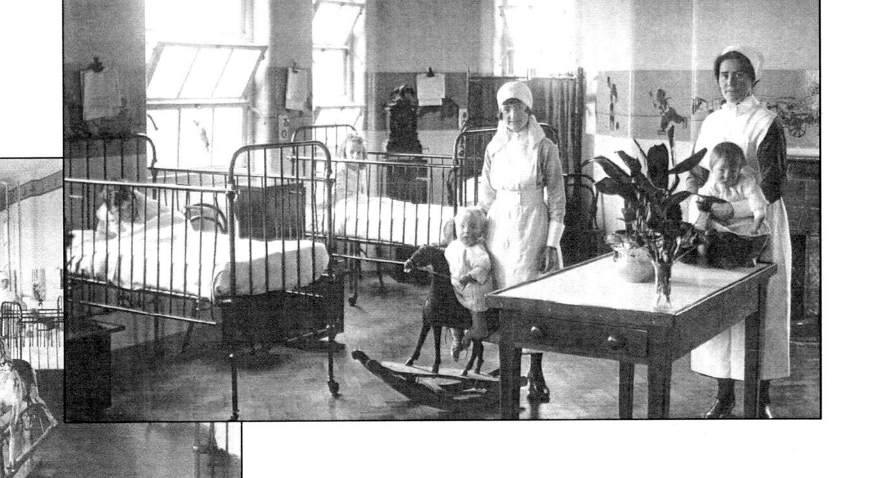

Above and left: Two views of the children's ward taken in the 1920s. [DRO]

the matron's quarters, and a suite of rooms for for the medical officer, and a board room, where meetings were held. In the 1950s, this latter room was used for nurses to collect their monthly salaries, which were handed out by the matron and the hospital secretary. Every nurse had to sign that they were in receipt of their money, the amounts of which varied according to their grade:

1st year student	£10-9s.-0d. per month for a 48-hour week
2nd year student	£11-9s.-0d. per month for a 48-hour week
3rd year student	£13-10s.-0d. per month for a 48 hour week

Close by, in a prominent position was placed a collection box for a particular fund which the nurses were all expected to contribute to!

A sharp right turn at the top of the stairs on the first floor led to a small corridor which gave access to the theatre suites and, on the far right, the main staff dining room. There was also a back staircase leading from the dining room to the lower floors, the main kitchens and a lift.

A further staircase led from the first floor to the second floor where large double doors led to the children's ward. The lift was situated near these double doors. On the children's ward, the patients were admirably catered for with both open-air and enclosed play-rooms. There were fourteen cots in the ward, and every possible amenity was catered for including such novel features as miniature washing bowls, baths, tables and chairs.

On the ground floor, some twenty-yards along the main corridor, on the right, a long corridor led to the out-patients department which had a south facing frontage and a driveway leading off Grove Park Road. It had a patients' waiting hall, consulting rooms, dressing rooms, massage rooms, dispensary, an up-to-date operating theatre and a recovery room.

The hospital, which was run under the supervision of the hospital management board, was financed by working men's contributions, donations and gifts from the public, general fund-raising, plus the interest from investments.

The William & John Jones Hospital

The William & John Jones Hospital was situated on Grove Park Road, alongside the out-patients department of the War Memorial Hospital. It had its own entrance.

The building was of two storeys, the ground floor ward accommodating twelve beds, a sluice, toilets and a sterilising room, with a large veranda on the south side, facing Grove Park Road. There was a ward kitchen and sister's office.

Stairs led to the floor above where, immediately on the left, was sister's office, a sterilising room and a single ward. On the right, the corridor led to a four-bedded ward, two two-bedded wards and three single-bedded wards, with bathrooms, toilets and a sluice half way along the corridor on the left. There was also a kitchen, a nurses' room and a visitors room on the main corridor.

At the top of the stairs, the corridor floor widened, and to the extreme right, was the pathology department. An electric lift completed this building.

Later, the William & John Jones Hospital, was incorporated into the War Memorial Hospital by means of an extension of the main corridor to the ground floor ward, which was called Morris Ward. The upper floor wards catered for the private patients. A few years later, possibly in the mid to late 1950s, a new corridor was built to the rear of Morris Ward's kitchen, which led off the main corridor in a northerly direction to the newly built Grove Ward.

The brothers William and John Jones should never be forgotten by the people of Wrexham and district, for they were extremely generous benefactors who donated many thousands of pounds for the care of the sick. They were also

HRH Prince Henry standing in the doorway of the William & John Jones Hospital during the opening ceremony.

Medical, nursing and administrative staff, War Memorial Hospital, April 1945.. Photograph taken outside the Out Patients Department. Seated L–R, commencing 6th from the left: Miss Stanley (Nurse Administrator); Dr Glyn Evans, Mr Richard Davies (Hospital Chairman); Matron Heeley; -?-; Dr Jock Reid; Dr Livingstone; Miss Price (Principal Tutor). Standing behind them L–R: Ted Ellis (Senior Laboratory Technician); 8th from left, Sister Edwards; 12th from left, Sister Senior. [DRO]

responsible for opening convalescent homes in Rhyl and Minera, and financed the building of St John's Church in Hightown (in memory of Mrs John Jones).

The progressive changes that took place in the Wrexham War Memorial and the William & John Jones Hospitals were:

In 1930 discussions were held regarding the building of a new nurses' home, and land was purchased for the sum of £2,000. The foundation stone was laid in 1933 by Sir Alfred Mc Alpine, president of the board of management. The total cost of building the new nurses home was £17,660. It stood on Chester Road on the site now occupied by the Nightingale House Hospice In 1934, Lady Howard de Walden, performed the opening ceremony, and the home was named 'Plas yn Llwyn'.

1935, the ground floor of 'Roseneath' (the private house originally built for civil engineer William Low) was converted into a new ward for male and female eye patients, the entrance to the ward being a little further up the main corridor from Pantomime Ward and, a little further up the main corridor still, a ward for male and female ear, nose and throat patients was created. This ward was situated opposite the corridor leading to the out-patients department. On the left of the entrance to the ENT ward were stairs leading to the upper floors where the nurses resided until Plas yn Llwyn was built in the 1930s. After this time, the upper storey of Roseneath was used as a doctors' residence.

1938, the foundation stone was laid for a new out-patients department by Mr Walter Roberts, JP, and was officially opened by him the following year.

In 1937 Mrs W. H. Evington donate the sum of £10,000 to build two new medical wards. These were built on the second floor of the main hospital building, adjoining the children's ward. The new ward, located above Overton Ward, was called Evington Ward and the new ward located above Cunliffe Ward was called Mason Ward. The layout and design of both wards matched that of the existing wards.
Under the will of J. G. Sudlow, a further sum of £30,000 was made available for extensions in 1946.

On 5 July 1948 the National Health Service came into being, and the Wrexham & District War Memorial Hospital and the William & John Jones Hospital were taken over by the Wrexham, Powys & Mawddach Hospital Board.

Volunteer stretcher bearers, May 1941. War Memorial Hospital.

The 'Elms', a large house situated on the corner of Rhosddu Road and Grove Road, continued to serve as a nurses home, catering mainly for those on night duty. 'Romano' another large residence with its frontage on Grove Road was the sisters home, and had a back entrance onto the hospital grounds. Later, 'Richmond House', situated on the left side of Grosvenor Road, was purchased by the Wrexham Powys and Mawddach Hospital Management Committee, as a residence for doctors.

Children's Ward

Situated on the top floor of the hospital, this was a very sunny, happy ward and catered for orthopaedics, general surgery, eyes and ear, nose and throat (ENT) cases as well as general injuries and road traffic accidents. In the 1960s, eye cases moved to the new eye unit at the Maelor Hospital and a little later, the children's ENT unit also moved to a new ENT unit at the Maelor. The age of the children was up to twelve years. Visiting was flexible, and parents were allowed to stay all day if they so wished.

When I was a staff nurse on the children's ward, I found the parents were more upset that their child was in hospital than the child was itself. Sometimes a child would start to cry when the parent or parents were leaving, and I would ask them to stay by the ward door, where there was a small window in the door, through which the ward could be observed. Ninety-nine times out of one hundred it was amazing how, within a matter of minutes, their child would settle and start playing with the other children or, if the child was a bed patient, other children who were up and about would come over to the child's bed and start amusing them. Children were good for one another.

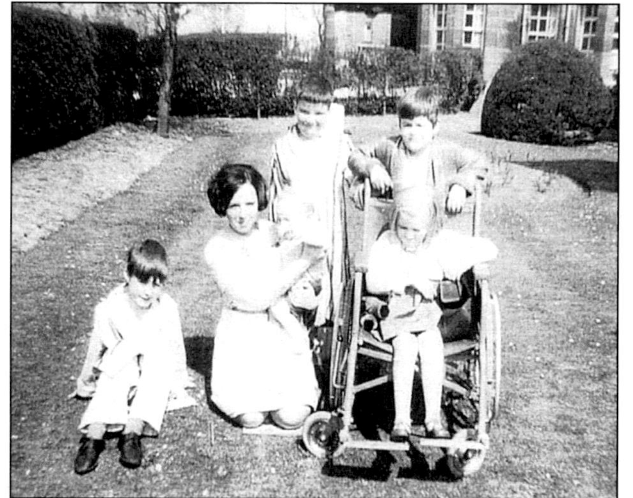

Children's Ward staff and patients, 1966.

Above: Student Nurse Buku with twin patients on the balcony.

Left: Mair Hughes (née Griffiths) outside Pantomime Ward, in the grounds alongside Rhosddu Road.

Above left: Student nurses taking a break during their final exams, c.1965.

Above right: Medical Ward staff pose on a ward balcony, c.1959. Front row: -?-; Sister Evans (Mason Ward) , -?-doctor, Sister Powell (Evington Ward), Student Nurse Perrin (right). Back row: -?-; S/N Wooton, Student Nurse Davies.

Left: Three nurse cadets, wearing their yellow uniform. Cadets, aged 16, were accepted from 1966, to gain experience before commencing their training aged 18.

Right: Sister Mills, night-duty sister, 1950s.

Below: Matrons Hague's retirement party, 1962.

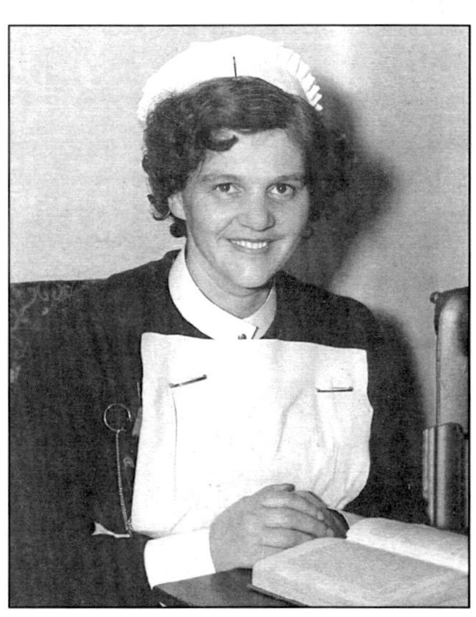

Nursing staff, War Memorial Hospital, 1960. Photograph taken outside the main door of the William & John Jones Hospital.

1951 Wrexham Carnival. Sister Ada Roberts (née Griffiths) on the float by the '1951' sign. [Mr Roberts]

Below left: The Children's ENT Ward with Sister Kay Allen (née Marshall) supervising.

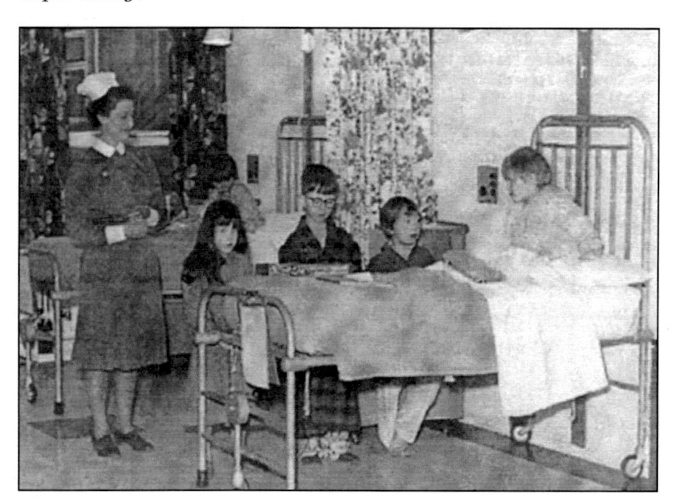

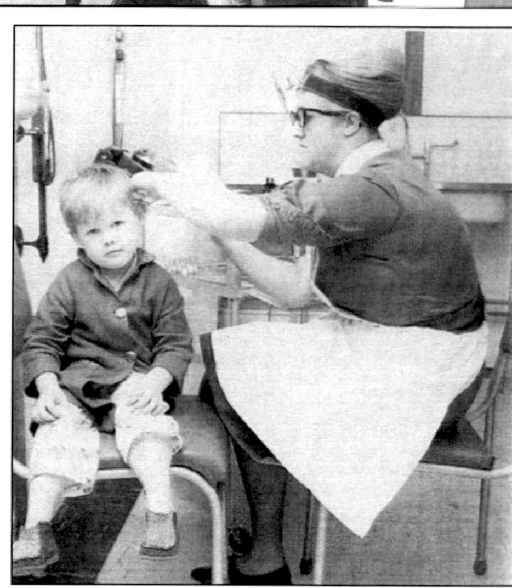

Right: Sister Moira Jones ENT ward sister carrying out an ear treatment on a little boy.

Miss Glenys Morgan

Ear, Nose and Throat Department (ENT)

In about 1948, Mr Aiyer was the first ENT consultant to be appointed in Wrexham followed some years later by Mr Barraclough. During the 1950s Sister Allen (née Marshall) was the theatre and clinic departmental sister. Sister Parry was the ward sister.

The ENT ward and department were transferred from the War Memorial to the new ENT unit at the Maelor Hospital in the late 1960s.

Audiology by Miss Glenys M. Morgan

April 1949 found me taking up a post in the War Memorial Hospital, for the purpose of setting up, and running a permanent hearing aid department in Wrexham. Previous to that patients were dealt with at intervals by a visiting technician from Cardiff.

On my first day I reported to the hospital secretary, Mr Lesley Spencer, who gave me directions on how to get to the ENT department where I was to work. I found the department, and apprehensively walked into a very large room in which sat a man in a white coat wearing a head-mirror, and mask. I assumed he was a doctor, and in fact the gentleman turned out to be Mr R. D. Aiyer, the senior ENT consultant. I opened my mouth to greet him, and he barked out, 'What do you want?' Not a good beginning you might say, but there was worse to come. He had not been informed of my arrival and asked where I expected to work since there was no room for me in the ENT department, at which point I nearly ran away! However, he relented somewhat, and said that somewhere would have to be found and, to my horror, he suggested that I use a very small brush cupboard, which housed the audiometer, the only hearing testing appliance the department owned. There was no air or natural light in the room, but I was told I would be given a fan — the disadvantage being that it was very loud and deafened everyone anyway!

After eighteen months of theses conditions — still in the brush cupboard, and working solo — I made a tearful plea to Mr Aiyer to improve things for me, and all I got was, 'Go away girl and stop crying'. However, the following day he sent for me, and with a broad smile informed me that I was getting an assistant — and Mr Glyn Phillips appeared. Soon afterwards we were moved into a large room in the 'Hostel', the house on the corner of the hospital grounds on Grove Park Road, opposite King Street. The pharmacy department was also situated there, and all I could say was 'God Bless Mr Aiyer', my life at work had certainly improved.

Dr Harry Jones, MC as an RAMC officer during the Second World War (above) and in the 1960s (left). He was also the staff medical officer.

The Orthopaedic Department

This could be found on the corridor between outpatients and the main hospital corridor, between x-ray department and the ENT theatre and clinic area. It consisted of one treatment room, two consulting rooms and an office. The corridor doubled as the patients' waiting area, with seats along one side.

The orthopaedic wards were Pantomime (female) and Prince of Wales (male) on the ground floor. Children's orthopaedics were on the children's card, on the top floor of the hospital.

In the 1950s there was just one consultant, Mr Rowland Hughes (who established an international reputation in children's orthopaedics, especially hip conditions), and one medical officer, Dr Harry Jones, who also doubled as a general practitioner and dealt with most

Facing page: Coronation celebrations, 1953. Staff and patients wait outside the War Memorial Hospital to see the Queen and the Duke of Edinburgh on their Coronation Tour of Britain.

Sister Edwards, sister on the private wing, receives her retirement presentation from Matron Hague, c.1959. [Mrs Nell Tyler-Jones]

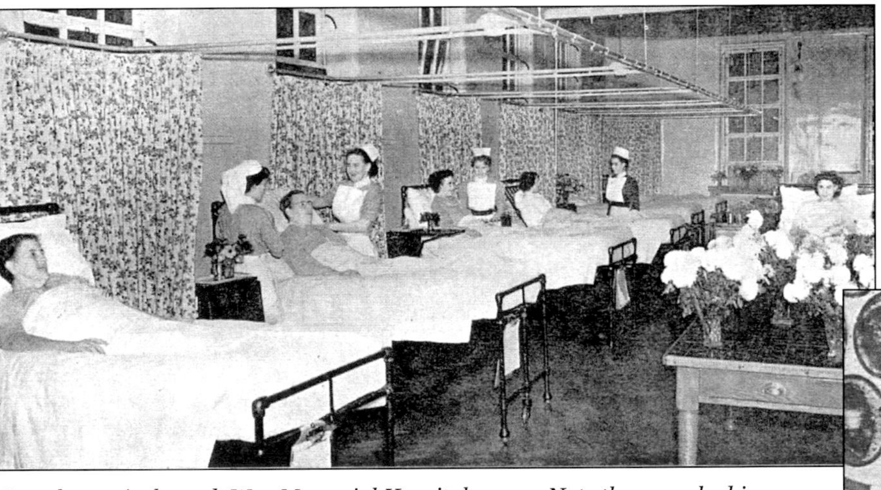

Female surgical ward, War Memorial Hospital, 1950s. Note the camp bed in the middle of the ward. When an extra bed was required the porters brought this type of bed up from the basement. Black in colour, they were lower than the other ward beds. In the early days each ward had a coke stove to provide the heating. It was the duty of the ward domestics to keep the stove topped up with coke and to clean it. The coke was brought up to the wards by the porters. These stoves had all disappeared by the late 1950s.

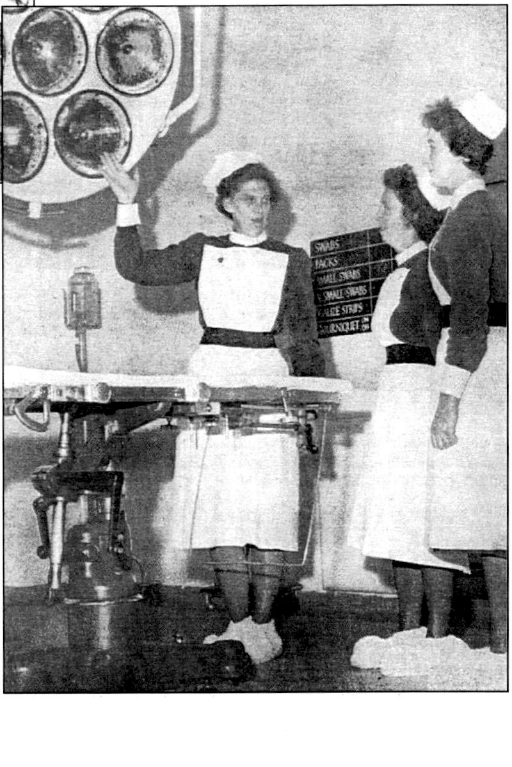

Senior Theatre Sister Glenys Jones shows two other sisters the new adjustable theatre light, fitted with seven high-powered lamps to provide a brighter light without shadows. c.1961. This equipment can be compared with the original theatre equipment shown on page 53.

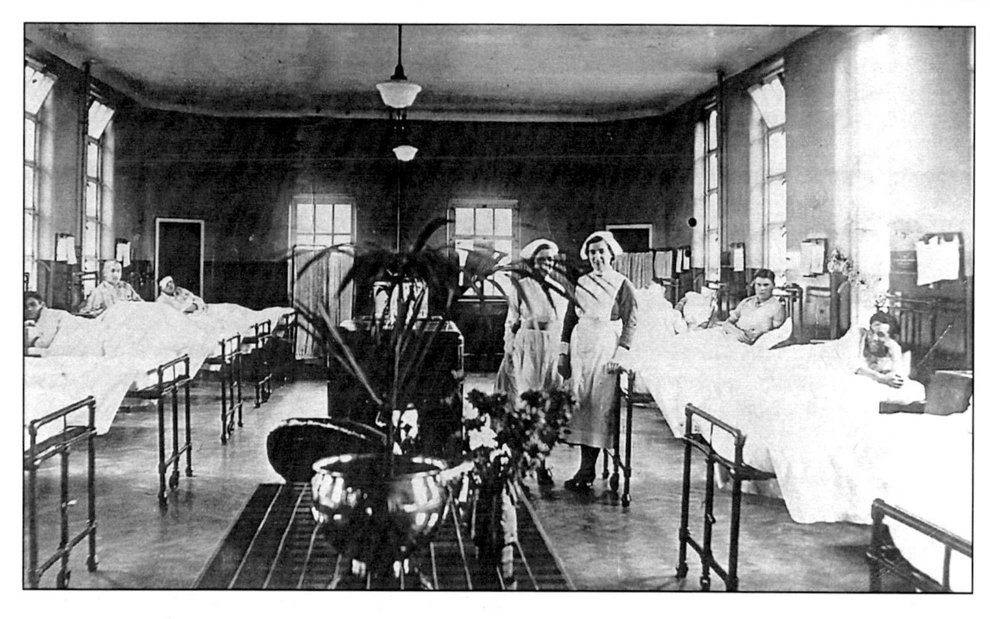

Male orthopaedic ward, 1940s. Sister Senior is standing on the right.

of the fractures. At the end of 1952, a medical rotational system began with the Robert Jones & Agnes Hunt Hospital, Gobowen. Registrars came to the War Memorial Hospital on a six monthly basis, the first was Mr John Aston. It was not until the 1960s that a second consultant orthopaedic surgeon was appointed — Mr Eurig Jeffreys.

The nursing staff increased from one sister, and two staff nurses, to three sisters and three staff and student nurses. Mr Harold Davies, an orderly, was trained to remove plasters, and carry out other practical procedures. Clinics sometimes ran into the early evening and nurses who should have been off-duty at 5pm just had to work through.

After-care staff came twice weekly (on Mondays and Fridays) from the Robert Jones & Agnes Hunt Orthopaedic Hospital. They held clinics with Mr Rowland Hughes, following up the care of mainly children, and assessing their progress. They also did home visits.

It was in the 1970s, under Mr Hughes' direction, that all clinical data relating to congenital hip disease and related disorders was stored on computer. Information from 3,000 cases was recorded on the regional computer in Birmingham, known as the Medical Information Retrieval Project Oswestry. Mr Hughes retired in 1980, and died in 1998.

Eryl Morgan, ex-orthopaedic departmental sister, Wrexham War Memorial Hospital

I did my general nurse training at the Liverpool Royal Infirmary from 1946–50. It was a voluntary hospital, and a deposit of £100 was required from every student before the commencement of training. This money was returned to the student on completion of training. Our intake did not have to wait this long, because the NHS was introduced in 1948 and and the deposit system was abandoned. We worked long hours and had one day off a fortnight.

After 'staffing' for a year, I went to London to do my midwifery training when my monthly salary was reduced to that of a student nurse — £6 per month — because I was undergoing further training! Despite this, however, we were still able to enjoy ourselves. Free theatre tickets were issued to the hospital every evening for staff to use and we were also allowed to take friends to the hospital canteen until midnight, where we could get beans on toast for 3d (1.25p).

After completing my midwifery

Mr Rowland Hughes and his wife at the unveiling of his portrait in the Institute of Orthopaedics at Gobowen, 1980.

training, I joined the staff at the Wrexham War Memorial Hospital as a departmental sister in 1952. The medical staff were a consultant, Mr Rowland Hughes, and medical officer Dr Harry Jones, who carried out reductions of most fractures in the department, and also took clinics. Dr Harry was also the staff medical officer and saw and examined all sick members of staff. It was very often the case that we assessed the casualty and, if we thought the fracture needed reduction and application of a plaster cast, requested an x-ray and had an anaesthetist on stand-by before Dr Harry arrived. During the day he had many commitments outside the hospital and he used to pop in and out, to keep an eye on things.

Clinic patient numbers were large, every patient was seen, and we often did not finish until 7pm (instead of 5pm) when we should have been off duty.

There was a very warm and friendly relationship between nursing and medical staff. Nursing staff were regularly invited to join the doctors with their wives at social functions either at their homes or in a hotel, and we were all collected and returned to the hospital by car. They were very happy times.

I left the War Memorial Hospital to have my son, and it was sometime later that I returned to nursing as a sister at Chirk Cottage Hospital.

Radiology Service by G M Murray, consultant radiologist

In 1941 Dr Stanley Nowell became the first consultant radiologist at the War Memorial Hospital. Prior to this appointment, Mr Reed a radiologist had run the department by himself. The department at this time consisted of two rooms: a diagnostic room and a therapy room. In 1951, Dr Ifan ap Thomas joined Dr Nowell and the x-ray departments in both the War Memorial Hospital and the Maelor Hospital were expected to provide modern x-ray facilities. Modern x-ray intensifiers and TV screen monitors were installed. Before this, the screening of work such as barium meals was performed in complete darkness which made many patients apprehensive. Radiologists had to wear red goggles to 'dark adapt' which also presented a weird image to the patient.

It was in the 1970s and 1980s that a revolution occurred in radiology, with the widespread use of other methods of imaging patients, and Wrexham was in the forefront in adopting this modernisation. In 1974 ultrasound equipment was purchased, becoming a five-roomed ultrasound department carrying out more the 25,000 examinations a year. Ultrasound was used initially for the screening of pregnant women, but is now used widely to examine other areas of the body.

In 1986, when the War Memorial Hospital closed, a new eight-roomed department was opened in the new Ysbyty Maelor and, due to the magnificent fund-raising appeal by (CHABS), a CT scanner was purchased shortly afterwards. With increased technology, imaging examination now has methods of showing patient anatomy and disease, and many patients are now treated by the radiologist's 'interventional' techniques, requiring only an overnight stay, which, 50 years ago, would have entailed major surgery and several weeks in hospital.

Above: Matron Hague and members of the Hospital Chaplain's Committee, 1950s.

Left: The War Memorial Hospital Chapel, which was opened in 1955. The building survives today, alongside the main entrance block at Yale College Wrexham and the windows have been transferred to the chapel at Ysbyty Maelor.

Patients and medical staff awaiting the arrival of HRH Princess Alexandra who stopped at the War Memorial Hospital en route to opening the new Guildhall in Wrexham, 7 July 1961.

Children's Christmas party at the War Memorial Hospital, 1955.

Hospital Chapel

Matron Hague was a very religious person and encouraged all her students to attend church or chapel. Before the War Memorial Chapel was built, it was the custom, that every Sunday morning, as many student nurses, and any other members of nursing staff were 'rounded up' and attended either the Parish Church or Bryn-y-Ffynnon Chapel's morning service. Nurses wore their full uniform and cloaks, and walked two-abreast with the home sisters in the lead. Later, a purpose-built chapel was constructed at the instigation of the Rotary Club of Wrexham. This was more convenient for everyone to attend services which were held in the mornings and, sometimes, in the evenings. Any patients wishing to attend, whether walking or in wheel chairs, were accompanied by their ward nurses. The chapel building stood alone on Rhosddu Road, alongside the main War Memorial building.

Pharmacy

The pharmacy was located in the out patients department. Mr Ralph Davies was appointed chief pharmacist in 1953. As the volume of work increased, the department moved to the house on the corner of Grove Park Road, opposite King Street which they shared with audiology, the hospital sewing room, the hospital almoner (Miss Roberts) and the medical secretaries. Shortly after this move Miss Vivien Lavis-Jones was appointed a senior pharmacist. In the mid to late 1960s a large pharmacy department was established at the Maelor General Hospital serving both hospitals. Mr Davies became Chief Administrator of Pharmaceuticals for both establishments. He retired in 1989.

Mr Ralph Davies, Chief Pharmacist.

Christmas at the War Memorial Hospital

At Christmas time rules and regulations were relaxed and the wards were made as happy and jolly as possible. There was great friendly competition between the wards to try to have the best-decorated ward in the hospital — inevitably a children's ward would win, usually with a lovely nursery rhyme theme. Only the patients that were tied to their beds due to fractures, or had under-gone recent surgical operations, or those who needed constant care, remained in hospital. Patients who had no one to help at home were also encouraged to stay in over the Christmas period.

On Christmas Eve, nurses, whether on or off duty, were encouraged to go around the wards carol singing. They would wear the reverse side of their cloaks uppermost, showing the red colour of the lining, which was very effective, and each carried a lantern. There was actually a nurses choir which sang many times in the Parish Church.

On Christmas Day, the ward routine was carried out quickly and efficiently and Father Christmas came to every ward and distributed presents to everyone. Christmas lunch was presided over by the consultant surgeon or consultant physician, who carved the turkey while the nurses distributed the meals. Visiting was usually flexible and during the afternoon visitors were allowed to stay for tea.

The nurses had Christmas lunch in two sessions, depending whether you were working a 'through-shift' or a 'split-

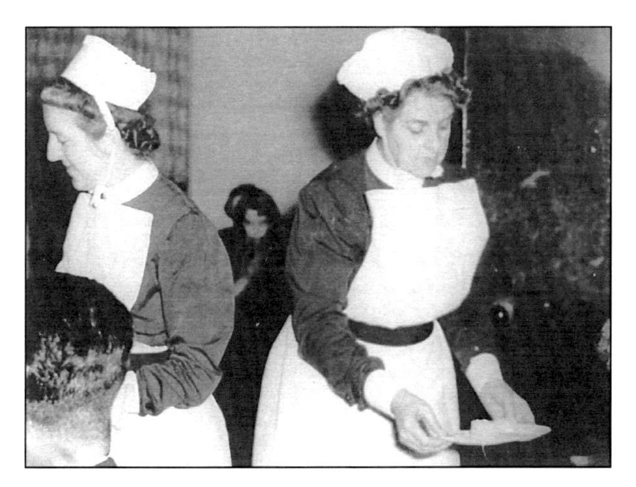

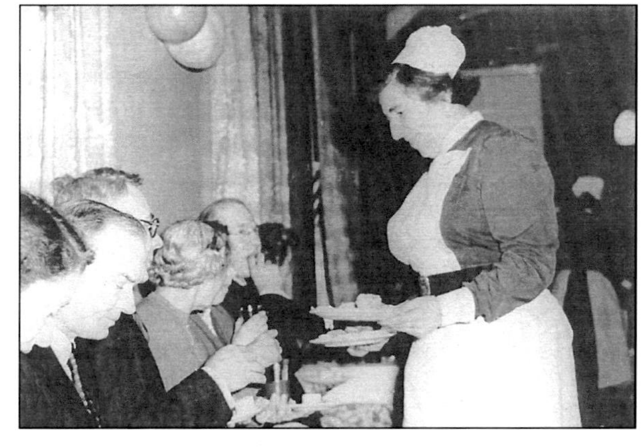

Nursing administrator, Miss Taylor Jones and Deputy Matron Miss Stanley (left) and Sister Senior (below) serving Christmas tea to relatives and patients.

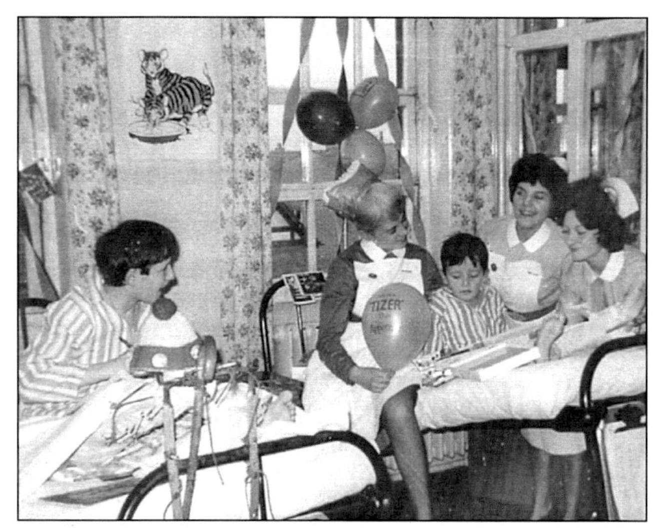

A children's ward at Christmas time.

shift'. They all ate a traditional Christmas lunch, followed by 'brandy-flamed' Christmas pudding and were waited on by the nursing administrators. Ward decorations were taken down the day after Boxing Day.

There was always a fancy dress party at the hospital on New Year's Eve; one that the author remembers clearly (around 1954 or 1955), was held in the casualty department, because it had a large hall (casualties being temporarily admitted to a different area of the hospital). I was a junior nurse and walking with friends down the long corridor to casualty, when there was a loud ringing of a bell and we had to spring quickly out of the way as a bicycle sped by with Sister Senior, pedalling furiously in a bow-legged manner, dressed in stripped trousers, black coat with flying tails, white shirt and bow tie, and wearing a moustache. She one of the strictest senior sisters in the hospital, we all had a giggle and thought she had been 'drinking'! The winners of the fancy dress competition that year were two staff nurses — one was dressed in a fur coat, with lots of jewellery and beautifully coiffured hair, the other in a wrap-over pinafore, with hair in curlers and a turban, smoking a cigarette and pushing a pram full of dolls (representing babies). Their theme — BEFORE and AFTER MARRIAGE! There was dancing and singing, especially by the Irish nurses, who did their traditional dances, and great jollity every where.

The following day it was back to the normal strict routine.

Reorganisation

By the late 1950s the War Memorial was becoming too small for the services and technological demands of the day. It was obvious that services were being duplicated at the War Memorial and the Maelor hospitals. The Wrexham Powys & Mawddach Hospital Management Committee were aware that there was an urgent need to upgrade the facilities of both hospitals and, in 1964, in conjunction with the Hospital Board, decided on a centralisation of specialities, and in preparation for this, and to meet growing needs, extensions and improvements were made to the x-ray and pathology departments and to the theatres. The plans to centralise the services in one building were vehemently opposed, partly due to tradition (there were those who favoured the War Memorial Hospital, and those who favoured the Maelor Hospital) and partly due to the belief that, if the problem was resolved, it might delay plans for a new district general hospital. The committee, however, thought that the vision of a new district general hospital was still a long way off and in 1966 an agreement was made to allow medical cases and clinics to move from the Maelor to the War Memorial whilst all general surgery was concentrated at the Maelor, thereby providing 170 surgical beds. Orthopaedic, private and accident and emergency care was centred at the War Memorial in a new wing funded by part of the Sudlow bequest. The old ENT and eye wards, which were part of the old Roseneath building, became the coronary care unit while the upper floors became the North Wales School of Radiography.

Plans were also made for the building at some future date of a new district general hospital based upon a 'nucleus plan' which was a standardised national design for hospitals. It was to be built in three phases. It was some twenty years later that the vision of this new hospital, built alongside the older Maelor General Hospital, was realised, at a cost of £14.5 million.

The last patients at the War Memorial Hospital, were moved to the new Ysbyty Maelor in June 1986.

The War Memorial Hospital was a beautiful building that the people of Wrexham were very proud of with wood block floors, wood panelling and an air of tradition and quality that engendered an *esprit de corps* in all who worked there, especially the nursing staff. It was an élite hospital for nurse training with an exceptional quality of patient care. Having heard of its good name, young ladies came from far and wide to train there including many Roman Catholic nuns. The people of Wrexham were proud of their hospital and regarded it with affection. It was their hospital, built with their money — coal miners being the biggest contributors. When wearing the War Memorial Hospital uniform, nurses were treated with respect. It was a sad day for everyone, when the hospital finally closed its doors but many look back at their time there with affection.

Chapter 8

Nurse Training

The following ruling, was found in an introductory leaflet which was given to those who wished to train as a nurse:

> Girls wishing to train as nurses, are expected to be of good education and physique, and between the ages of 18 years and 32 years of age, and 'Have a real love of her fellow-men, and realise that both the preventative, and the curative aspects of a nurse's work demand a spirit of service, needing patience, an equable temperament, sense of humour, determination, and the courage of her convictions.'
>
> A nurse is a professional woman, trained to be the skilled, intelligent colleague of the medical staff with whom she is fighting to prevent and cure disease.

Prior to training, a satisfactory medical, and dental certificate had to be produced and, on being accepted for training, a Mantoux test was carried out to see if they had immunity to tuberculosis. If the test was negative a B.C.G. injection was given, and a further Mantoux test was carried out later. If the test again proved negative, the person was unable to produce an immunity to tuberculosis and was deemed unsuitable for nursing. A smallpox vaccination was also given to all students — which made everyone off colour — and most were also given a chest x-ray.

Plas yn Llwyn

This nurses' residence consisted of four floors and more than 50 single rooms. There were 12 or 13 rooms on a corridor, with communal bathrooms and toilets. At the end of each corridor, was a larger room, which was usually occupied by a sister, or senior staff nurse, who were roomed there specifically to keep 'law and order'. The more junior the student nurse, the higher the floor, their room was on — a first year student was on the top floor. There were no lifts, you just climbed up each flight of the marble mosaic patterned stairs. It was just unfortunate for you if you forgot something, after leaving your room, you just had to trailed all the way back.

Everyone had a single room, which had a single bed, a wardrobe, a dressing table, a wash hand basin and a chair. The mattress was made of 'horse hair' and was very hard. When the students became more senior, they gradually moved

Plas yn Llwyn Nurses Home, Chester Road, Wrexham. Just visible is the illuminated pathway leading from the hostel to the War Memorial Hospital. Part of the Wrexham inner ring road went through the grounds in the 1970s and the home was demolished in the 1990s to make way for the Nightingale House Hospice. [WAWC]

Prize Day, 1943. Photograph taken outside Plas yn Llwyn.
Front row L–R: Sister Price, -?- , -?- , Matron Heeley, Mrs F. W. Morris, -?-.
2nd row: Miss Taylor Jones (in army uniform), other unknown.
3rd row: -?- , Mr Richard Davies (Hospital Chairman), -?- , Dr Glyn Evans.
Back row L–R: Dr Livingstone Pow, Dr John Reid, -?-.

down a floor, and the mattresses became more comfortable!

On the ground floor, was the students' sitting room, in latter years equipped with television, radio and a piano. The trained nurses had their own sitting room. There was also a communal kitchen and laundry area.

The Home Sister and the Principal Tutor each had a room on the ground floor. To the rear of the ground floor were the lecture rooms, and practical room.

The general daily routine began when a maid knocked on the doors of all rooms at 6.30am; if you did not wish to be called, you pinned a note to your door. Beds had to be stripped, and the linen folded and put neatly outside your door every Monday morning, ready for laundering. Maids, working under the supervision of the Home Sister, made up the beds with clean linen, and cleaned the rooms.

The steps coming from the main door of 'Plas' led directly to a flag-stoned path, which went to the War Memorial Hospital, and there were electric lights along the way. A couple of these flag-stones were loose, and anyone walking over them especially at night, made an almighty bang, alerting the Home Sister that someone might be coming in late without a pass! To avoid these in the dark you had to walk several yards on the grass verge. This path to the hospital skirted around the hard and lawn tennis courts, which staff used regularly during the summer months. Before reaching the hospital, students passed the boiler rooms and other out-buildings on the right.

Breakfast was from 7am in the main dining room at the hospital. No aprons were worn in the dinning room, they were put on in the changing room attached to every ward. On entering the dining room, there was a table on the right, where the nursing administrative staff sat for their meals. All staff had to acknowledge this 'hierarchy' and excuse themselves as they passed through the door. If anyone failed to do so, they were called back and had to apologise. An administrative sister who was in charge of the kitchen gave the meals out; in my day it was

Nell Tyler and colleague pose for a photograph after collecting their SRN prizes in 1954.

Sister Senior who kept a close eye on whether the students ate all their meals.

At the bottom of the dinning room was a large table for the 1st year students. Then a table for 2nd year students, a table for 3rd year students, 4th year students and staff nurses seemed to share the same table, and finally a table for the sisters.

From 1939 to 1955 butter and sugar were rationed. Each student was allocated 2 ounces of sugar and 2 ounces of butter per week, which was collected every Monday morning, from Sister Senior in the main kitchen. As you may imagine, this amount only lasted a couple of days, and the rest of the week you had to make do with margarine, which was freely available on the dining table, and had no sugar in your tea!

Tutors, late 1960s. L–R: Mrs Gwyneth Jones, -?- , Mrs Megan Jones, Miss Muriel Owen, Miss Doreen Pritchard.

Most lectures, given by doctors or tutors, were in your on-duty time. If they happened to fall in your off-duty time — tough luck, you still had to attend.

On day duties nurses worked a 48-hour week, with 1 day off, and a half-day on alternate Sundays. Night duties allowed nurses two nights off every 14 days. Over the years the hours of duty per week have decreased, a working week now being 37 1/2 hours, and two days off per week, and night duty staff have four nights off a fortnight, and an extra night off every two months.

Everyone had to be in by 10pm during week-days, and 10.30pm on Saturdays. If a nurse wished to stay out later, a late-night pass had to be obtained from the matron. Of course, there were always ways around this and girls occupying the ground floor rooms would let students who had no pass in through their window. If 'Alfie' was the night porter, we got in without problems.

All students had to be resident until they passed both parts 1 and 2 of their preliminary state examinations. State examination fees of 7 guineas (£7.35) had to be paid by the student. When they successfully passed parts 1 & 2 the students were given a £5 bonus and were allowed to live out; the board and lodging money, which had previously been paid to the hospital when living in, was then added to their salary.

In 1954 students at Strathalyn, Rossett were paid £6 per month, later increasing to £7.35. On passing the P.T.S. examinations the monthly salary increased to: 1st year students — £11.45 per month; 2nd year students £12.35; 3rd year students £13.50.

All nurses were on duty at 7.30am prompt, either working a straight shift until 4.30pm (with a lunch break), or having a split shift working from 7.30am to 2pm, then 5pm to 8pm.

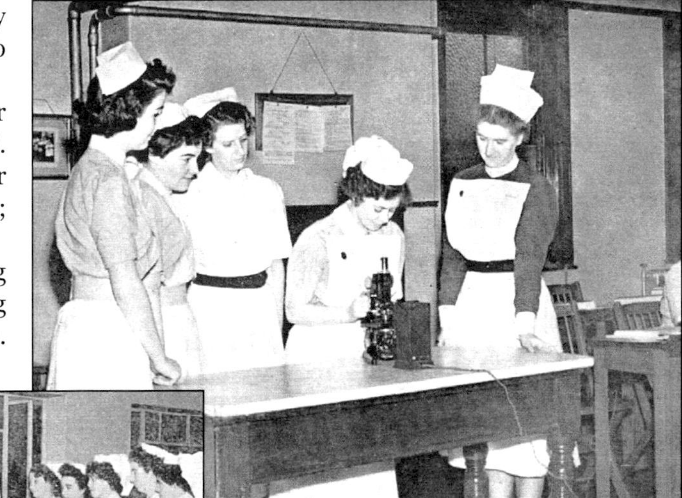

Above: War Memorial Hospital, Sister Tutor Williams demonstrates how to use a microscope.

Left: Practical demonstrations by sister tutors at the War Memorial Hospital, 1956. This 'ward' was equipped with beds and dummy patients.

Prize Day, c.1950, Plas yn Llwyn.

Prize Day, William Aston Hall, 1957.

Prize Day, Plas yn Llwyn, 1950s.

Prize Day, 1956.

Night staff worked a twelve-hour shift from 8pm to 8am. Sisters had their breakfast at 7.30am and came on duty at 8am.

Matron, or her deputy, carried out a ward round each morning and evening, but one never knew at what time she would be coming. Everyone tried to make themselves scarce, but she visited the kitchen, the laundry room, and the sluice — there was really nowhere to hide. She would call you to her, and ask you the reason why a particular patient was in hospital, and what treatment, or clinical tests they were having. This made every nurse swot up each case in the ward — which was not a bad thing.

Any nurse who broke a thermometer whilst taking temperatures had to take the thermometer to Matron and state how it was broken. Later, the broken thermometer had to be taken to the pharmacy where it would be replaced. Much later still, the broken thermometers were just placed in the ward dispensary basket and a new one ordered.

Breakfasts were served to the patients at 7.30am followed by bed-pan rounds, and bed making. Beds would be drawn into the middle of the wards, patients who were mobile would be encouraged to go to the day-room, bed patients would be covered by their blankets. Windows would be opened at the top and bottom to allow fresh air to come into the ward through the lower part, and the foul air to pass out through the top half of the window. Damp dusting, with cloths soaked in antiseptic, was carried out by the junior students on every ward. The ward domestic swept at the back of the beds with damp mops, and then 'came the polishing'.

By 9am everywhere was 'spick and span', lockers having been cleaned and covered jugs of fresh water with upturned glass provided for each patient. Someone else would put out the freshly watered flowers — if someone mixed red and white flowers sister would raise the roof for this was the gravest sin as old suspicious staff said it was the sign of death on the ward.

If there was a theatre day on the ward, the routine was slightly changed and ward cleaning had to be carried out quickly to facilitate the preparation of the theatre patients. On a non-theatre day, everything was got ready for the doctor's round. Sister or staff nurse would be getting things ready for this 'round', preparing case notes and getting x-rays and path lab reports ready.

Consultants rounds were usually carried out once a week but the house officer and registrars came on daily visits. Most consultants entered the ward at 9am for the 'round'. They would have quite a retinue of staff following them, registrars, house officers, physiotherapists and a secretary. This was thought to be one of the best ways of learning and medical and nursing students were asked questions and patients were encouraged to ask questions about their treatment. Sister or staff nurse would visit every patient and explain the 'case' and notes would be made of any requests, or advice made by the consultant or registrar.

'Idle hands' were not encouraged in nursing. During visiting hours, it was the custom to place a student nurse at the entrance of the ward, and they had to ensure that there were no more than two visitors to a bed. During this time the nurse had dressing and swab drums on a bed table in front of her, which had to be filled up ready for sterilising. Other students were sent to do other tasks, such as work in the sterilising room. Needles had to be tested for bluntness, (the needle was drawn across a piece of gauze, if it caught a thread this meant it was blunt and had to be discarded and replaced by a new one). Needles were then placed in fresh methylated spirits in rectangular glass dishes with stainless steel lids, as were glass syringes. Rubber gloves had to be filled with air to see if there were any leaks, these would then be patched, powdered, and placed, according to size, in glove drums for sterilising (there was a great deal more of this work to be done if you worked in theatre). The steriliser had to be emptied daily, and cleaned and instruments, stainless steel bowls, receivers, galli pots etc. were boiled for ten minutes.

Nurses were not allowed to wear make-up or jewellery, and their uniform had to be immaculate. Black stockings were worn along with the correct black footwear. If Matron saw a nurse with a ladder in her stockings she was sent off duty to change them. Everyone was issued with a navy woollen cloak with red wool lining, which had red tapes that crossed over the chest and fastened at the back under the cloak — a smart asset to the nurses uniform, and an absolute 'godsend' in the cold weather. First year students wore grey-stripped dresses, white starched 'Peter Pan' collars, white belts and white starched butterfly caps. Second year students (who had successfully passed their parts 1 and 2 exams) wore grey-stripped dresses, stiff white round 'dog collars', starched stripped belts and small white caps. Third year students wore grey stripped dresses, round white collars, small white caps and a black stiff belts. Fourth year students wore mauve dresses and belts with white stiff collars — they had successfully obtained their hospital finals certificate and were awaiting their state final examination results. Staff nurses (who were fully trained SRNs) wore royal blue dresses, white round collars, white caps and stiff blue belts. Sisters wore navy dresses with long sleeves with white starched cuffs, white round collars, small white frilled caps and stiff navy belts. Matron wore a grey dress with a fine linen cap and delicate lace cuffs. Matron Heeley, appeared to be the first matron, and was in office throughout the Second World War. She was followed by Matron Hague who retired in 1961. Matron Bridger (Queen Alexandra's Royal Army Nursing Corps) took over, and wore a plain navy dress, white lace collar and cuffs, and small white lace cap. In my student days the deputy

Wrexham School of Nursing Prize Day, 1966.

Wrexham School of Nursing Prize Day, 1967. Guest of Honour Air Marshal Frederick Rosier.

Wrexham School of Nursing Prize Day, 1968, photographed outside Maelor General Hospital Chapel. Guest of Honour G. Prys Davies, Chairman Welsh Hospital Board.

Wrexham School of Nursing Prize Day, 1969, photographed outside Maelor General Hospital Chapel. Guest of Honour, Lord Kenyon.

Left: Student nurses receive anatomy lessons in the training school.

Below: Sister Nell Tyler-Jones demonstrates how to pass a Ryles tube to a group of student nurses.

Left: Student nurses in a children's ward play area.

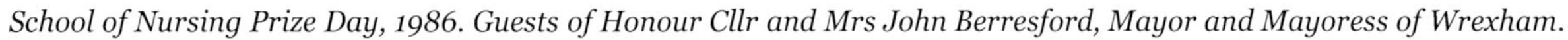

School of Nursing Prize Day, 1986. Guests of Honour Cllr and Mrs John Berresford, Mayor and Mayoress of Wrexham.

matron was Miss Stanley, who wore a dark green uniform with delicate lace cuffs, a collar and a hat tied with a bow under the chin. Miss Taylor Jones (home sister at the Elms) wore a brown dress with fine lace cuffs, a collar and a hat which was tied with a bow under the chin. Miss Norman (home sister at Plas yn Llwyn) wore the same uniform as Miss Taylor Jones. Miss Taylor Jones and Miss Norman also carried out ward and department rounds in Matron's absence.

Quite a few nurses took their caps, collars, and belts, to the 'Soo Ken Chinese Laundry' in Brook Street, Wrexham. These people were masters in the art of starching; there was a distinct sheen on the articles and they would be a great deal stiffer, and last much longer than when starched in the hospital laundry. Belts could remain stiff and shining for up to four weeks.

My memories during 1954/5 when I resided at 'Plas' until I was successful in passing my preliminary state examination (Parts 1 & 2) when I was allowed to live at home for the remainder of my training. Students were not allowed to try these examinations more than twice in Wrexham and failure meant they were either allowed to leave their training, or had to transfer to another hospital.

The Maelor Hospital became a training school for nurses in 1956, and joined the War Memorial Training School, which then became the Wrexham School of Nursing. Theoretical and practical training and lectures were continued at the War Memorial class rooms in Plas yn Llwyn.

School of Nursing Prize Day, 1987. Guests of Honour Cllr and Mrs Arthur Evans, Mayor and Mayoress of Wrexham.

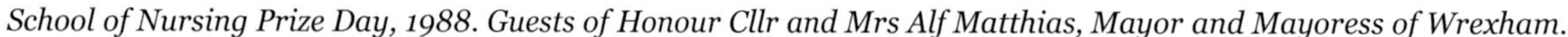

School of Nursing Prize Day, 1988. Guests of Honour Cllr and Mrs Alf Matthias, Mayor and Mayoress of Wrexham.

Strathalyn Preliminary Training School for Nurses

This large, beautiful mansion in Rossett was opened in 1952, as a preliminary training school for nurses where they completed a three month residential training course. If they lived near enough, the girls were allowed home at weekend,s otherwise they remained at Strathalyn for the duration of the course.

The course covered various subjects e.g. anatomy, physiology, hygiene, care of a sick patient and practical instruction (making beds, learning various lifting techniques, trolley and tray setting, first aid and the cooking of invalid diets).

Mornings were devoted to lectures. After lunch students attended the demonstration room for instruction. It was also during the afternoon that visits were made to the local sewage works, water works and creamery factories to study the technique of pasteurisation of milk and the sterilisation of bottles. Two evenings a week were spent on the wards in the one of the hospitals. All lecture notes had also to be copied-up in a personal file each evening.

At the end of the three months there was both a written and a practical examination. The students who were successful gained entry into the War Memorial Hospital where, after a one week break, they started their training for the State Registered Nurse qualification (SRN).

The Home Sister in my day was a Miss Robins. A tutor gave lectures in the mornings, and another gave practical instruction in the afternoons. Living conditions were very comfortable, and the meals were exceptionally good. We were all very happy there.

In 1962, due to the changes in the nurse training structure in Wrexham, Strathalyn was closed.

Above: An informal teaching group in the study room at Strathalyn.

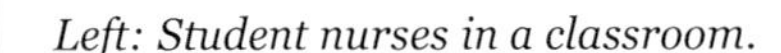

Left: Student nurses in a classroom.

A group of student nurses meet up with the ambulance staff, c.1970.

Strathalyn Preliminary Training School, Rossett, 1952–62

Left and below: Strathalyn, Rossett, the Preliminary Training School for Nurses. The house still survives but is now private apartments.

Left and below: Groups of students in the grounds at Strathalyn, 1958. The tutor in the centre of the group on the left is Miss Muriel Owen. [Eirlys Perrin]

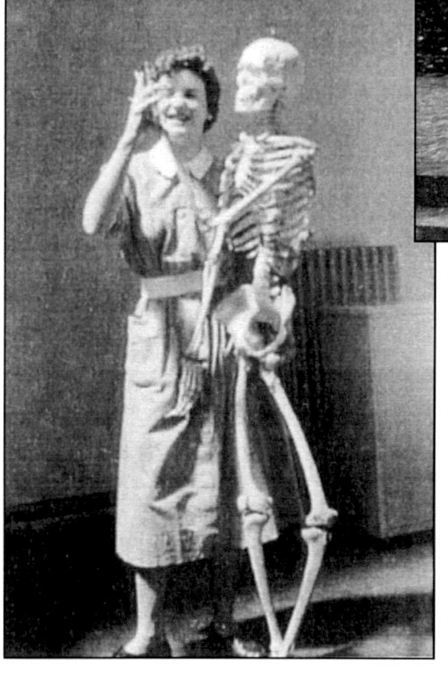

Left: Student Eirlys Perrin with 'Jimmy' the skeleton. [Eirlys Perrin]

School of Nursing Prize Day, 1990. Guests of Honour Cllr and Mrs Cyril Williams, Mayor and Mayoress of Wrexham.

School of Nursing Prize Day, 1992.. Guests of Honour Cllr and Mrs D. J. Roberts, Mayor and Mayoress of Wrexham.

Chapter 9

Maternity & Paediatrics

Midwives

There were no trained midwives until the Midwives Act of 1902 was passed. Most women, especially the working class woman in childbirth, was attended by the 'handy woman' who was not a professional person, more likely an older woman who had gained experience by having her own babies, and helping with other members of the family who were in childbirth. These people practised right up to the late 1930s. A doctor was rarely called for because a fee had to be paid to him, and many women were unable to meet the cost. The only time a doctor was called was when there were complications.

Some of these 'handy women' were dirty, drink-sodden old hags, without skill or conscience, the 'Sairey Gamps' (named after the notorious birth attendant in Charles Dickens's book *Martin Chuzzlewit*). Their standard of hygiene and childbirth skills were non existent, and their practice was very detrimental to women in childbirth, causing increases in the maternal and infant mortality rate. However, there were those 'handy women' who were very experienced in childbirth care, with good standards of hygiene, and the expertise to recognise when labour or childbirth were not following the normal course, who would send for the doctor post-haste.

Most doctors recognised the qualities of a good 'handy woman' and were quite happy for them to practise in their area, and often referred pregnant women to them. Sometimes the 'handy woman' provided the mother with extra help, taking in the washing, cleaning the home, preparing food for the mother and even helping with child care.

Local 'Handy Woman' — Summerhill area, Wrexham by Mrs Joan Chaloner

My grandmother Sarah Ann Dodd, died in 1953, nearly eighty years of age. She was one of the 'handy women' described above, and practised in the Summerhill area. She cared for people who were sick, tended the dying and laid them out. She also attended women in childbirth, and the lying-in period.

My grandfather was a 'chalter master' at Westminster Colliery and worked in the coal mining industry all his working life. He was a strong believer in herbal medicine, and this was obviously the cheapest way of dealing with minor ailments and sickness, especially since he and my grandmother had a large family. His remedies were written in a book, and my mother remembered quite clearly being asked to go to Ffrwd wood, to pick various herbal plants. My grandmother would use these potions when caring for her patients.

Grandmother, was small in stature, and had a very pleasant disposition. She was recognised and remembered by the locals for wearing full-length, pure-white aprons. Before attending a patient she always tucked the corners of her apron into her belt, thus keeping the inside of it clean. If the mother she had delivered was poor, she would supply soup or stew during the lying-in period, and also did any washing that was required. The lying-in period, lasted for up to 14 days, but she attended the mother for longer than this if there was a need. My grandmother paid a young girl from the village to help with the washing and to do some of the general housework.

During the late 1930s, a little girl was knocked down and killed by a bus in one of the lower villages. She was six years of age, a beautiful child with blond curly hair. Her family were very poor and in need. My grandmother purchased a lovely white silk dress to lay her out in, and one of my first recollections was of attending this little girl's funeral. I must have been two to three years of age. I was holding my mother's hand and there appeared to be a great many people present. They were lined up and walking slowly towards the house, and going inside. My mother and I followed and, on entering the living room, there was an open coffin on the table, which was in the centre of the room. The people were walking around the table in a clock –wise and orderly direction, to see for the last time this beautiful little girl, and to pay their respects. I did not quite reach the height of the table, so I did not see anything.

My grandparents had a large house with an 'ever open door,' and anyone requiring help would walk in, knowing that she would always do her best for them.

Local 'Handy Woman' — Broughton Parish, Wrexham,
by Mrs Dinah Hughes.

Mrs Catherine Jones was a local personality of the Pentre Broughton area being their unqualified midwife. Born in 1846 she died in 1933, and will probably be remembered by some of the older residents of the community as 'Nain Galed'.

She was a very hardy lady, and the nick-name was bestowed on her because her husband Robert who was called 'Galed' (hard or strong) after a courageous act during the 1889 explosion at Brynmally Colliery. The explosion occurred on 13 March when Catherine and Robert's son, Thomas, was killed. Robert was awarded a medal for bravery for attempting to rescue some of the miners. He found that his son was dead, and carried the body of the young man all the way home, which was quite a distance, and no easy feat. Hence the name 'Robert Galed' was bestowed on him.

Mrs Catherine Jones, Nain Galed, with one of her grandsons, her last delivery.

Catherine was an unqualified midwife covered the whole of Broughton parish, and sometimes beyond, always having to walk to her patients homes. During her time as a 'handy woman' she delivered 2,000 babies and was always quick to call a doctor, should any complications arise.

Nain Galed, was undaunted by the weather. Like all mothers and midwives she knew that babies did not always choose the best time to be delivered. In winter, when snow and ice made walking difficult, she would put socks over her boots, in order to make walking easier. Her grandson would quite often accompany her on night journeys, carrying a storm lantern, which was big and heavy.

Often, if the family had no one to do it, she would bring washing home and would take gruel or soup for the mother. Her daughter made the soup and did the washing.

Her charges would seem ridiculous to us today — 21/- (£1-1s.-0d.) which covered the cost of the delivery and fourteen days attendance during the lying-in period, sometimes visiting twice a day if it was necessary. A shilling was always given back as a present for the baby, and sometimes if the family were too poor to pay, she would waive her charges. Nain's services were always in great demand, particularly to one family, where she delivered fourteen babies.

She was eighty years old when she finally gave up work as an unqualified midwife, or 'handy woman', delivering her last baby on her eightieth birthday, this baby being her grandson. She was awarded a silver medal for delivering 2,000 babies, and for her good work in the community.

The first Midwives Act was passed in 1902 and, like other medical and social reforms, this was slowly implemented. In 1903, the Central Midwives Board approved a three months period of training after which the candidates were tested by means of oral, practical and written examinations.

New legislation came in in 1915 whereby the notification of new births to the medical officer of health after 28 weeks gestation was made compulsory. This had to be carried out by the midwife after every birth. The 'handy women' could not do this and to get around this legislation, doctors allowed them to practice under their guidance and the doctor notified the births.

In 1918 the doctors fees and mileage expenses was placed on the local authorities who would, if possible, recover the cost from the mother. Midwives expenses received consideration and they were compensated for any loss of earnings if they had a compulsory suspension from duty due to the attendance of a patient with infection, or the delivery of a 'still birth'.

The 1934 Annual Report of the Central Midwives Board recorded that anyone practising as a midwife without qualification, were liable to a fine of £5 or 28 days imprisonment.

Example of a Midwife's Tariff.

- 1st Confinement 42/-
- 2nd Confinement 40/-
- Twins 10/- extra
- False Alarms 2 /6
- Nights 5/-
- Long Distances 50/- possibly for a taxi cab fare.
- After waiting over 4 hours there would be a charge of 1/- per hour thereafter.

In the 1930s ante natal care was introduced. It was realised that care and support were required in the ante natal, labour and post natal periods, and

The 'Old Wife' and a newly qualified midwife after the 1902 Act.

that the midwife's duties were to embrace all aspects of the mothers welfare. By 1936, the vast majority of students taking midwifery courses were already State Registered Nurses, but not many of them practised midwifery after qualification.

The statutory duties of the midwife included

1) To obey the rules of the Central Midwives Board, as laid down in their handbook.
2) To notify the local supervising authority of her intention to practice midwifery in that area, at the commencement of practice, and on the 1st January of every year, and to notify any change of name or address.

The handbook of the Central Midwives Board, incorporated the rules and code of practice which the midwife was expected to follow and which every student and practitioner of midwifery should not only possess, but be familiar with.

A midwife who was present at the birth of a baby which was unlikely to survive has the authority to baptise and give a name to the infant in the absence of any clergy.

The Midwives Act of 1936 revolutionised the standards and practise of midwives. For the first time, there was a system where the midwives were given regular periods of off duty and annual leave as well as financial security (including a pension) and the provision of a uniform and equipment.

The Nurse by Shirley Randles (née Parry)

I was born in May 1935 the daughter of 'The Nurse' who was my mother Mrs Edith Parry. She returned to her post of district midwife when I was six weeks old. Her employing authority was the Denbighshire Nursing Association. She did her general nurse training in Chester, and fever nurse training at Bucknall Isolation Hospital, Stoke-on-Trent. My grandmother paid for her to take her midwifery training in Dundee. The trainee midwife had no salary and had to supply her own uniform. My grandmother used to tell me how she had to send food parcels for my mother and her friends, because they were so ill fed. As a child I remember our household revolving around 'her district' as she called her work. She covered the areas of Broughton, Moss, New Broughton, and Southsea. She walked to all of her calls, until she had a car in 1951.

I remember when I was at grammar school not seeing her for five days, as she had gone from one delivery to another, plus seeing her other patients, and just catching a couple of hours sleep whilst I was at school. Thank goodness my grandmother lived with us.

Broughton and district was a mining area and some of the people were very poor.

My mother's fee was (£1-1s.-0d.) which paid for the delivery, and her care for fourteen days post delivery, visiting twice a day for the first few days. I remember spending many an evening, sitting at the kitchen table making cotton wool balls from a roll of cotton wool, the fluff going up my nose and making me sneeze! Also cutting squares of cardboard out, and covering them with gauze, a piece of tape was stitched on either side as ties, these were used to cover the umbilical area of the new born to give support and keep the area flat. The 'Old Wife' in the old days used a penny and a binder for this purpose. They were placed in biscuit tins, and baked in the oven of our triplex grate. This was the only way that nurses and midwives could sterilise their dressings at that time.

In the early days antenatal care was non-existent, and my mother worked very hard trying to introduce this care to the area. I remember the ladies always coming after dark, usually bringing a friend to accompany them. It was all very secretive being 'booked-in' and our second lounge became a consulting room, with a locked cupboard, a couch on which were folded white sheets, and four chairs. My mother told me later that many husbands were against their wives attending these types of clinics, as they believed their wives should not 'show themselves' until ready for delivery.

My grandmother, who lived with us also thought it a disgusting practice, and did her best to make her views known to the ladies, if she could catch them! she would hang around by the back door waiting for the ladies to come out, until my mother found out!

As already mentioned parts of my mother's working area was very poor, and there were large families. When visiting these families my mother carried with her a large zipped bag, in it would be sticks to light a fire, usually neighbours would provide coal. Very often miners sold their coal allowance to buy food, and clothing for the family, if they were off work through injury, there was no income. She often took bread and jam etc. to the houses where it was needed. Sometimes the bottom drawer of our large wardrobe had to be taken to put the new baby in, and there was always a set of baby clothes in the airing cupboard, for families who had nothing. In this type of case the neighbours rallied round providing more baby clothes, and gave any other help required. Although poor, this type of community was very close, with neighbours helping one another. My mother always tried to stress the importance of hygiene in these areas, to no avail, and always marvelled that cases of 'Thrush' were almost unknown.

In Poolmouth Valley, (later to be called Moss Valley) Romany gypsy families stayed at certain times of the year, and many travelled miles to come back to the area if there was someone near her time for delivery. When my mother entered the caravan they made her very welcome, and were always very grateful for anything that was done for them. Before anything was discussed they insisted on showing my mother their marriage certificate, that is if my mother did not know them very well, they also showed her the 'layette' which was always ready for the birth. Nurse was always invited to the christening of the new baby!

In the 1950s Trevalyn Manor Hospital became a Part II training school for midwives, and pupils were allocated to my

A new delivery at the Poolmouth Valley gypsy camp in the 1940s. The same families came to the camp on a regular basis every year. The photograph shows relatives from a neighbouring caravan, posing for their picture to be taken of the new baby, and the midwife, Nurse Parry. [Mrs Shirley Randles]

mother for three months (district midwifery training). They 'lived-in' at our house, and when my mother talked to them about her midwifery experiences they were astounded, and found some of them very hard to believe. During her time as district midwife in the Broughton area she delivered 1,600 babies, and sadly died six weeks before her retirement. Her ambition was to write a book on her memoirs as a midwife, and although her book was never written, I am able to give to you and others who knew her, some of my memories of her life, and recall some of the stories she told me.

Ruabon County Maternity Hospital

Ruabon Hospital was a striking building. It was largely black and white on the front and sides, and there was a wall in front of it, which was continuous with the wall of the Primitive Methodist chapel, which went along the High Street, and retained the Doctor's Field. 'Kandy Lodge' was not there at this time. The grounds were fairly spacious and were kept in order by Mr Harwood, of Mount Pleasant, Ruabon. During the 1930s and1940s he was the pumper of the organ at Ruabon Congregational church.

In 1935, Mr Robert Owen Jones was appointed county consultant obstetrician and gynaecologist for Denbighshire, and he regularly travelled to see patients in the various clinics, covering an area as far south as Welshpool and Dolgellau. Drs Lawton Roberts, Turner and Davies, the Ruabon general practitioners carried out work at the hospital.The hospital anaesthetist was Dr Steven Jones, who died when he was in his early forties.The matron was Miss Lilian Lee, a very strict, religious person who insisted that all mothers be 'churched' before their discharge. Patients came to Ruabon from as far afield as Abergele and Colwyn Bay.

Mr Robert Owen Jones was a very popular man, skilled at his work and quite a character. Medical colleagues said that he had a very quick brain, and was exceedingly talented. One of his colleagues, an anaesthetist, remembered a young German refugee doctor coming to work under Mr Owen Jones in a Wrexham hospital and, whilst he was operating in theatre, Mr Jones carried out a conversation in three languages — German, Welsh and English. He was a very fine artist and often drew pictures in a patient's case notes, to try an illustrate either the type of operation he had performed or the picture the patient was presenting prior to diagnosis. When carrying out correspondence with GPs regarding their patients whom he had seen, he would often resort to poetry. Amusing and a great person to work with, he would sometimes suddenly quote a passage from the Bible or Shakespeare. He had a marvellous memory and could remember patients from as far back as twenty years, and he always had something special to say to each one. He always had something pleasant to say to the most junior probationer nurse and, of course, became the 'idol' of his day, not only with his patients but also with

Ruabon County Maternity Hospital.

Left: Mr Robert Owen Jones, County Consultant Obstetrician and Gynaecologist, 1936–59.

Right: Ruabon Maternity Hospital midwives and babies, 1937. L–R: Enid Jones, Phyllis Edwards and Muriel Davies (later Matron at Gerwyn Hall, Gladwyn , Trefalyn Manor and Maelor Maternity Unit.

nursing staff. Mr Owen Jones carried out his own post-mortems and research on babies. Mr Robert Owen Jones retired in 1959 and was succeeded by Mr David Barry Beckweth Whitehouse.

The birth registers 2 November 1938–27 March 1947 show many stillbirths and a large number of perinatal deaths (death during the first week of life) as compared with the figures of today. Bearing in mind that the statistics were over period of nine years, there were 30 sets of twins, 4 maternal deaths and a few caesarean sections.

Ruabon County Maternity Hospital was closed in 1947 with the services being transferred to Trevalyn Manor Maternity Hospital in Rossett. Sir Watkin Williams Wynn then offered the building to the parish of Ruabon as a non-political and non-sectarian social centre, as a memorial to his father. A local poll rejected the offer and the building was demolished in 1960.

Gerwyn Hall

Gerwyn Hall was originally owned by Mr and Mrs Gossage. He was a member of a soap manufacturing family from Birkenhead and she was related to the Tate & Lyle sugar manufacturers. Shortly before the outbreak of the Second World War, Mrs Gossage, who was then an elderly widow, gave Gerwyn Hall, with all its contents, for the use of evacuees and the wives of servicemen from the Birkenhead area. She moved into the chauffeur's cottage and, a little later, became unwell and went to stay at Ruthin Castle Nursing Home, where she later died.

Gerwyn Hall was converted to a maternity home, mainly for women who had been evacuated from the Birkenhead area. Mr Owen Jones, the county obstetrician and gynaecologist was placed in overall charge of the facility with Miss Muriel Davies, who had been a midwifery sister at Ruabon Maternity Hospital, serving as matron and Dr Kasper, an Overton general practitioner, looking after the mothers and babies.

The first admission in the register of births was on 2 September 1939 and 52 patients were delivered from September 1939 to 2 March 1940. Gerwyn Hall was then closed because, at that particular time, there had not been any bombing of the Merseyside area and the women returned to their homes in Birkenhead and the Wirral. Most of the midwifery staff moved back to Ruabon Hospital.

On 13 April 1941, due to the blitz on Merseyside, Gerwyn Hall

Gerwyn Hall, Marchwiel.

was re-opened, but this time the running of the maternity home came under Denbighshire County Council. A mixture of patients admitted, some from the local area and the remainder from the Birkenhead and Wirral areas.

When it was a fine day, the midwives were instructed by Matron Davies to carry the babies, out to the lawn in their cots, making sure they were in the shade. The cots would be covered with fine nets for safety. She was a great believer in babies having plenty of fresh air.

On Mrs Gossage's death, Gerwyn Hall was left to her sister, who sold it in 1946 and patients and staff moved to Gladwyn Hall, Gresford, in September of that year.

Statistics

The statistics cover both periods (2 September 1939–2 March 1940 and 13 January 1941–26 September 1946)

Births, 3,031.
Peri-natal deaths (death within the first week of life), 16
Neo-natal deaths (death within 28 days of birth), 1
Stillbirths, 39
Twins, 15
Miscarriages, 4
Caesarean sections, unrecorded (according to staff who worked there, they were carried out, although not many).
Maternal deaths, unrecorded (they did happen, although not many).
According to the birth register for this period of time, two patients — one 12 days post-natal and another 8 days post-natal) were transferred to the Maelor General Hospital and, although there was no reasons given, they may quite possibly have been for the removal of 'retained products of conception'.

Gladwyn Maternity Home

Gladwyn, Gresford.

Gladwyn was built *c.*1850 and stood in 29 acres of land. It was a three-storied stone building with a southern aspect. It originally had twelve bedrooms, with dressing rooms, linen closets, W.C., bathroom and two staircases. The ground floor comprised an entrance hall and vestibule, a morning room, a drawing room, a conservatory, a housekeepers room, a butler's pantry and the usual domestic offices, with excellent wine, and ale cellars in the basement. The grounds were park-like in character, well timbered with fine oak and other trees. There was an ornamental pond at the foot of the slope from the house. The gardens and pleasure grounds were tastefully laid out, and contained two conservatories, rose gardens, tennis and croquet lawns.There was a good kitchen garden, which was always well stocked, with fruit and vegetables. There was also good stabling for eight horses, with a shippon, piggeries, a boiler house and out buildings. At the entrance from the main road, stood the lodge, and the house was approached by an attractive drive.

The first owner of Gladwyn appears to have been a Colonel White and there is a plaque, dated 1888, dedicated to his memory in the north aisle at All Saints Church, Gresford. In the early 1900s the Soames family, well-known Wrexham brewers lived there. Mr Soames died in 1932. In 1939 Gladwyn was taken over by the government to accommodate children that were to be evacuated from London in case of war. Mrs Soames who was elderly, moved out to the Lodge.

In September 1946, Denbighshire County Council, following the sale of Gerwyn Hall, Marchwiel, took out a lease on Gladwyn which temporarily became Gladwyn Maternity Home until Trevalyn Manor had been altered to become a permanent maternity hospital some nine months later. During the nine months that Gladwyn was a maternity home the following were recorded:

Deliveries, 395.
Twins, 3
Stillbirths, 3
Miscarriages, 1
Peri-natal deaths, 4
Neo-natal deaths, 3
Caesarean sections, none recorded
Maternal deaths, none recorded

While the maternity hospital was accommodated at Gladwyn Dr Christia F. Lucas, was appointed as resident medical officer. She looked after the mothers and the babies, with Miss Muriel Davies as matron. Overall charge of the unit lay with Mr Owen Jones, the county Consultant obstetrician and gynaecologist.

Wrexham Nursing Home, 22 Grosvenor Road, Wrexham

This 1930s private maternity home was located in a large semi-detached house on Grosvenor Road. Some time in the early 1940s when the home combined with the house next door to become a much larger nursing home under the control of the matron, Miss Menna Weaver Jones. Ante-natal care was provided by the patient's own general practitioner. The patient was taken into the maternity home when established in labour, and delivered by their own GP, with a trained midwife in attendance. Mothers were usually low-risk cases, any high-risk cases being delivered in the local maternity hospital.

The home closed in the mid 1950s and anyone wishing to have private care was accepted in the private wing at the War Memorial Hospital, or the private wards at Trevalyn Maternity Hospital. The Grosvenor Road nursing home was demolished in the mid 1950s and the new telephone exchange was built on the site.

Memories of Nurse Nora Crump

General Nurse Training in my day began at the age of 19 and lasted for four years. I did general nurse training at Chester Royal Infirmary and was fortunate to get both the gold and silver medals and a scholarship prize valued at £20 which I put towards the cost of my midwifery training that had to be paid for by the pupil. This training lasted for six months was taken at White Friars, Chester.

Retired midwife, Nurse Norah Crump.

I remember quite clearly when, as a pupil midwife on the district, having to deliver twin boys at home. You might think that this was not unusual at that time, but these twins were born six days apart. The first baby was born by normal delivery, the second twin was born six days later. The cord from the first twin lay clamped with a Spencer Wells forcep in a receiver. During the six days, careful watch was kept, and the area kept as clean and sterile as possible. I was allowed no time off duty during these deliveries. The second twin had an uneventful normal delivery, both babies and mother were in good condition.

During the 1920s and 1930s a scheme was introduced to enable people meet the cost of a district nurse or midwife, by paying 1d. a week. Various works such as Brymbo Steel Works, Westminster and Gwersyllt collieries, the local brick works, and many others, deducted one penny a week from their employees pay. Those not employed by such firms arranged for a person to collect the money from their homes. The District Nurses Association formed a committee to govern this fund, and the money went towards the payment of salaries etc. The Doctor was paid for his services in a similar manner. This system continued until the NHS came into being in 1948.

I started as a district nurse/midwife in 1942 after having my own children. My colleague, Nurse Matthias of Bradley (who is now in her 90s), and I travelled around on bicycles. Nurse Matthias was the first Queen's District Nurse in this area.

The analgesia (pain relief) at that time was oral, and then the Minnitt machines were introduced in 1936 which gave inhalational gas and air. This machine was invented by Mr Minnitt an obstetrician at one of the Liverpool hospitals. Training in the use of this machine was taken by all the Wrexham and District midwives at Trevalyn Manor Maternity Hospital. Gas and air was given to mothers in normal labour, to help alleviate pain.

On the District, this rather cumbersome Minnitt machine was included in the equipment which had to be carried by the district midwife, as well as the delivery bag, record books and other accessories, which made life very difficult when there was only a bicycle for transportation. We were then advised to take driving lessons. When they became competent drivers, some midwives used a county car, or van whilst others were able to use their own vehicles, and be reimbursed travel costs.

Our bags — delivery, post natal, and drug bags, and our record books were all inspected by the supervisors of nurse/midwives at regular intervals. An inspector accompanied them on her rounds to ensure standards were maintained.

All district nurses/midwives belonged to both the Royal College of Midwives and the Royal College of Nurses, which were the governing bodies, and in midwifery we adhered strictly to the Central Midwives Board rules and code of practice.

During my time on the district, it was quite a regular thing to be called out to mothers in labour who had received no ante-natal care. One such case which sticks in my mind was when I was called out to a mother who was in advanced labour in a remote cottage in a place called Windy Hill. On quickly examining her I discovered she was having twins, and immediately sent for the doctor. The twins were born before he arrived, and fortunately mother and babies were in a satisfactory condition. Within twelve months this same mother delivered another set of twins, but because she had ante-natal care this time, things were more orderly and the doctor was there for the delivery. I attended this mother 10 times for deliveries over the years.

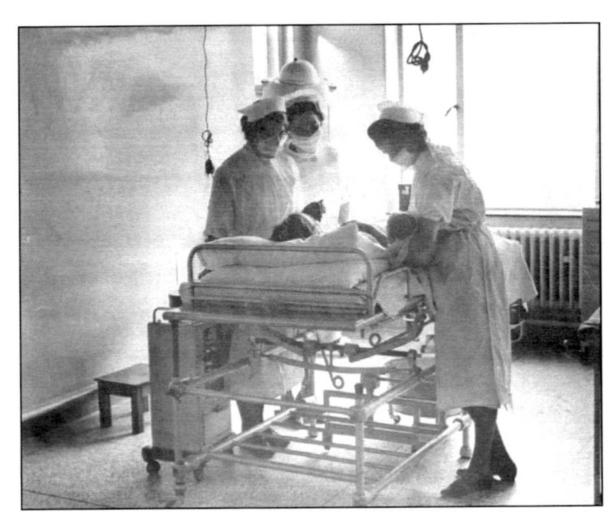

Joan Britton, a Part II Pupil Midwife (left) at the Maelor Maternity Unit, 1963.. [Joan Britten]

Memories of Midwifery 1962–97 by Sister Joan Britton

I remember my midwifery training as though it was yesterday! I commenced training in May 1962 at Sorento Maternity Unit, Birmingham. On the morning I was to start my training, I said goodbye to my mother who was poorly and in bed, and made my way to the station, and was most surprised to see her at the station, ready to wave me off. I cried all the way to Birmingham.

Work at Sorento was very hard and the hours very long. If the unit was busy during the night, pupil midwives would be called out of their beds to help, irrespective of whether they had to get up for the early morning shift. Night duty was long and hard. Patients were of mixed race, with dark to light coloured skins, which coming from Wrexham I had never seen before. During the night pupils had to relieve the other midwives for their meals. On one particular night I had to relieve Block A, then go on to Block B and so on, with extremely long corridors to walk in between wards. Every ward was busy, with babies crying everywhere, or so it seemed at the time. I just wearily plodded on, from one ward to another, gave a crying baby to it's coloured mother, hoping a good feed would quell some of its noise, and carried on with other work, a little later I returned to remove the now satisfied baby, to its cot in the nursery. The mum said 'I have fed this one nurse, if you bring me my baby I will feed him as well.' She did not appear to mind in the least feeding someone else's baby, but was my face red!

All pupil midwives had to witness the birth of ten deliveries before they could then have hands-on experience of five deliveries with a trained and scrubbed midwife in attendance. At my first 'witness' delivery I fainted!

I passed my Part I midwifery examination in November 1962 and in December 1962 commenced my Part II midwifery training at the Maelor Maternity Unit, Wrexham. This entailed three months in the hospital, and three months in the community under the supervision of a trained midwife. Many babies were born at home at this time and the midwife and I travelled around on bicycles. I qualified as a midwife in June1963 and sadly, just before my state results were received, my mother died. As a newly qualified midwife, I was offered the post of community midwife in the Wrexham area which I accepted and have worked as a community midwife ever since.

I passed my driving test in October 1963 and was issued with a Denbighshire County van for a while, until I obtained my own car. A few months later, midwives were issued with their own telephones. In 1964 I qualified as a Queen's District Nurse/Midwife.

I must mention that in the earlier days of my community midwifery, we did not have the sterile delivery packs,that we are fortunate to have today. They are prepared by the Central Sterilisation Department but we had to do our own. All the requisites for a delivery, were placed in a cleanly lined biscuit tin, one for the mother and a smaller one for the baby. They were placed in the oven for one hour, to render the contents sterile. Now and again the tins were over-baked if we were called out to an urgent case, the tins would be black! For sterile water, lemonade bottles were used, and filled with boiled water.

In 1968 I bought my first car, a Morris Minor Convertible, how I enjoyed that car. As the car got older, during the windy weather the hood would lift up and blow down. At this particular time I had a nun as a pupil midwife with me, and in those times they wore the nun's habit. We were travelling to see a patient one windy day when the hood of the convertible decided to blow up in the air, and drop back, unfortunately it took the nun's head veil with it and as I could not stop the car at that moment because the road was busy, it did cause some embarrassment I can tell you.

As this car got older it became difficult to start at times, but I was never short of helpers to give me a push. On this particular day I could not start the car despite helpers pushing, so I had to call the garage and the mechanic came out with his towing vehicle. He hitched the

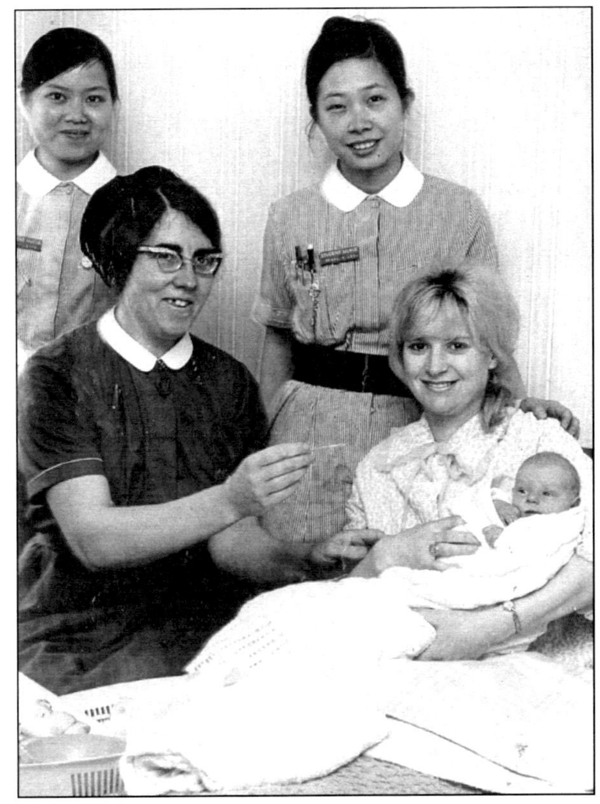

Sister Joan Britten makes a post-delivery visit accompanied by two student nurses. [Joan Britton]

Morris to the tow–bar and towed it back to the garage. When he arrived at the garage he found a couple of pounds of sausage on the roof of the car — someone had put them there so that they could push the car.

I had a boxer dog called Bruce, who came out with me on my nightly calls. When I left the car he would immediately get into my seat and not take his eyes off the house I was visiting. He was great company on dark nights.

During the winter of 1970 the telephone company's employees were on strike, for three days. Midwives placed a list of their calls in the windows of their homes, so that people would know where we might be. The police did a great job during those difficult times. They traced me to my various calls on a few occasions, when someone was in labour, and on one occasion, they were looking for three midwives at the same time.

In 1972 the car radios were fitted and came under ambulance control. Midwives were called 'Radio Mike'. This system was very useful. On one occasion I remember getting an urgent call from control, for a midwife. I changed the direction of my car, and rushed to the address given. On arrival I found that Jennifer was in advanced premature labour. She was thirty weeks gestation (42 weeks full term). There was a breech presenting with a footling hanging down. Jennifer had a safe delivery of a baby girl, weighing 2lbs. I was able to use my car radio to call a 'Flying Squad' from the maternity unit, who sent an ambulance, paediatric doctor and nurse and an incubator. Mother and baby were transferred to hospital. Baby Nichola is now a lovely young lady.

I always enjoyed being with the mothers and babies and their families, and nothing pleased me more than to hear members of these families call me Joan. However, it appears that now I am delivering babies of the mothers that I have delivered, is there a message there?

Joan retired in April 1997.

Trevalyn Manor Maternity Hospital

Trevalyn House was built in 1754 by William Travers (who died in 1765). The building was three storeys high and built of brick, with dressed stone quoins, and rustic lintels. It had seven bays, and a large wing with bay windows, and a doric porch, which was built on later. The interior was beautiful and spacious, with an oak well staircase (which remains today), sweeping up from a large hall with corner landings, ornamental stair ends, and a swept rail with columnar balusters. There were clusters of fruit intricately moulded around the ceilings. Chimney pieces were fitted with very elaborate fire places; one in particular was of marble in the corinthian style inscribed 'W.T. 1754' (William Travers). The families who occupied it over the years were the Travers, the Langfords and the Townsends. Trevalyn House became known as Trevalyn Manor.

On the out-break of the Second World War, Denbighshire County Council obtained tenders for the erection of a maternity home of 45 beds to be built on a site which they had acquired at Minera. This maternity home was intended

Trevalyn Manor.

Trefalyn Manor Maternity Hospital, 1950s

Trevalyn medical, midwifery and nursing staff, 1959. Front row L–R: Sister Thomas, Sister Edwards, Mr D. B. Whitehouse (Hosp. Chair.), Matron Pritchard, Sister Tutor, Dr C. F. Lucas, I. Jenkins (Hosp. Sec), Sister Edwards.

Sister Bellis.

A group of midwives and nurses.

Trevalyn Matron Pritchard with ancillary staff, 1959.

Trevalyn Management Committee, 1959.

Sister Phyllis Edwards, 1950s.

to replace Ruabon Maternity Hospital, which had only twelve beds, the majority of which were being used for special cases only. Due to the financial pressures of war, the Council was unable to proceed with the building and, after the war, a home for the care of the elderly was built on the Minera site.

In 1946, Denbighshire County Council, acquired this beautiful manor, and converted it into a maternity hospital for the area which was opened on 21 May 1947, by the Rt Hon. Aneurin Bevan, MP, the Minister of Health. Trevalyn over looked 60 acres of delightful park land, used for agricultural purposes, with beautiful stately mature trees.On the ground floor there were: a nursery with 20 cots, a premature babies room, one ante-natal ward, two post-natal wards, a consulting room, a milk room, a large general kitchen, a switch board, the matron's office and other administrative offices. On the first floor there were: a nursery with 20 cots, five small post-natal wards, a first-stage labour room, a labour ward, a theatre, a duty room and various other offices. An isolation block, comprising three separate rooms, with toilets and bathrooms, situated on their own corridor, came off the main corridor. On the second floor there were: the residential quarters for the matron, doctors, deputy matron, midwifery tutor, nursing and domestic staff. The sewing ladies also had a room on this floor. In the grounds there were a small nurses home, the head gardeners cottage, the assistant gardener's cottage, the handyman's cottage, stables, glasshouses (which were well stocked, with tomatoes, grapes, etc.) and well-stocked fruit and vegetable gardens.

The first matron was Miss Lilian Lee who was transferred from Ruabon Maternity Hospital along with her staff and patients. Nellie, was her maid, and she was married to the head gardener. The assistant matron was Miss Muriel Davies. Matron Lee retired within a few months of coming to Trevalyn and was succeeded by Miss Davies. She later married and became Mrs Pritchard, she and her husband lived near Trevalyn Manor.

The first resident medical officer was Dr Christia F. Lucas. In 1950 the first new county consultant paediatrician, Dr E. G. G. Roberts, was appointed, based at the Maelor Hospital, who visited Trevalyn Hospital regularly. The county consultant obstetrician and gynaecologist was Mr Robert Owen Jones.

In July 1948 the hospital came under the over-all care of the Welsh Regional Board, and the direct care of the Wrexham Powys & Mawddach Management Committee.

In 1955, Trevalyn Manor Hospital became a training school for Part II midwifery students.

Trevalyn Manor Maternity Hospital closed on 31 December 1959, and the patients and staff moved to the up-graded Maelor Maternity Unit in Wrexham.

On 1 January 1960, after substantial alterations, Trevalyn Manor became a hospital for the care of the elderly.

Retirement of Sister Phylis Mitchell (née Edwards) who had been a midwife at Ruabon, Gerwyn, Gladwyn, Trevalyn and Maelor Maternity Hospitals. Presenting her with a gift is Mr Barry Whitehouse while Miss Jean Cranfield (principal nursing officer midwifery) and Mr Arnold Humphreys (consultant) look on.

Wrexham Maelor Maternity Unit 1970. This picture was taken on the Labour Ward. Front row L–R: Enrolled Nurse Olive Richards, Staff Midwife Lily Lloyd. Second row: Sister Joan Chaloner, Night Superintendent Gwyneth Hughes, Midwifery Tutor Laura Jones, Night Sister Eleanor Jones. Third row: Student Midwife Chris Chievski, Dr Papasoterou, Chinese Student Midwife, Night Staff Midwife Noreen Power-Jones Night Staff Midwife Milicent McCarthy. Pupil midwives wore a mauve short-sleeved dress and belt, with stiff white collar and plain white cap. Enrolled nurses wore a green short-sleeved dress and belt, with white stiff collar, and plain white cap. Staff midwives, wore a mauve short-sleeved dress and belt, with stiff white collar and white frilled cap. Midwifery sisters wore a royal blue long-sleeved dress and belt, stiff white collar and white frilled cap. Labour Ward superintendent and night superintendent, wore a dark red long-sleeved dress and belt, stiff white collar and white frilled cap. Midwifery tutors wore a long-sleeved green dress, stiff white collar and white frilled cap. Matron wore a long-sleeved, pale grey dress of a fine material, with white lace collar and cuffs.

Maelor Maternity Unit

Mr David Whitehouse (County Obstetrician and Right: Gynaecologist) and Matron Muriel Pritchard welcome the Duchess of Gloucester when she came to officially open the Maelor Maternity Unit on 17 November 1960. It was the duchess's husband, Prince Henry, who officially opened the War Memorial Hospital in 1926.

Left: Building of the new wing at the Maelor Maternity Unit, 1974. Mrs Grace Wilden (Nursing Officer) with the trowel and midwifery sisters Joan Chaloner and Eileen Davies holding the wheelbarrow. This photograph was taken outside the upper floor of the building (Lawson Tait Ward), the lower floor being Simpson Ward.

Above: Sister Chaloner receives a cheque in support of the Labour Ward from the Wrexham Ladies Police Club, c.1980.

Left: Sisters Joan Chaloner and Beth Jones receive money collected by a group of Caergwrle youngsters, 1981.

Staff Midwife Eileen Edge in the post natal ward.

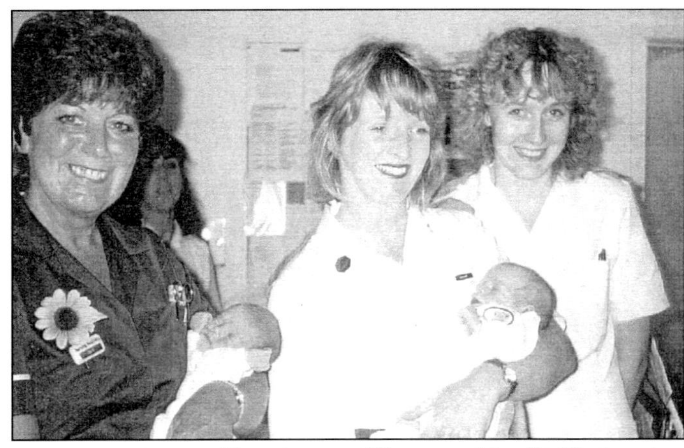

Nursing Auxiliary Susan Williams, and Staff Midwives Ann Keeleney and Anne Aitkins on the post natal ward.

A group of midwives photographed in their indoor uniform.

Maelor Maternity Unit

By the end of December 1959 the Maelor Maternity Unit, complete with ancillary facilities of 56 beds, was provided by adapting and altering the existing building, and later an ante-natal clinic was linked to the department. Later extensive improvements and alterations to the premature baby unit were carried out. The new complex, cared for maternity (with its Special Care Baby Unit), gynaecology, and paediatric departments.

On New Year's Eve, 1959, on the closure of the Trevalyn Manor Maternity Hospital, the staff moved to the newly up-dated Wrexham Maelor Maternity Unit which continued to be a Part II training school for midwives. Matron Pritchard remained in charge, with Mr D. B. Whitehouse as county consultant obstetrician and gynaecologist, Dr C. F. Lucas as resident medical officer and Dr Gerald Roberts as paediatrician. Miss Jess Cranfield, the night superintendent, became day labour ward superintendent in 1963, when Mrs Gwyneth Hughes became night superintendent.

In 1964, Mr Arnold Humphreys, an ex-R.A.F. Wing Commander (Medical Branch), was appointed as a new consultant obstetrician and gynaecologist. Those of us who worked with him, will always remember him with affection, he was one of us! Small in stature, he oozed personality. His teaching rounds on the wards and in the clinics, were of an exceptional standard, indeed many midwives owe him a great debt of gratitude for getting them through their final midwifery examinations. He was also an examiner with the Midwifery Board of Examiners. His generosity did not stop with midwifery, he helped many staff who had personal problems. He loved a joke and many were the times I've seen him coming down the corridor towards the Labour Ward, telling a joke to a porter, or other member of staff, their chuckles reaching us in the office. His patient care was of an extremely high quality, and his doctor/patient relationship was kind and caring. It was a very sad time for us all when, as a relatively young man, he died from leukaemia in November 1972. His illness was very short, and during the time he was in hospital he asked all his labour ward midwives and other staff to visit him. He was very sadly missed.

Matron Pritchard retired in 1968 and was succeeded by Miss Cranfield. At this time the title 'Matron' was changed to 'Principle Nursing Officer (Midwifery)'.

In 1970, Dr Lucas retired, having worked tirelessly in the profession, giving a lot of her time to the care of the unmarried mothers in the area. She had carried out two ward rounds each day, and was very fastidious in her scrub up technique prior to the examination of a patient, whether on the ward or in the labour area. As you might guess her house officers picked up this fastidiousness, because she could be very strict — not a bad thing.

Around 1970, the maternity unit became a Part I as well as Part II training school for midwives.

In August 1970 Mr Aled Williams was appointed consultant obstetrician and gynaecologist. He had been senior registrar in obstetrics and gynaecology at St David's Hospital, Caernarfon. He was a very well-liked person, able to speak both Welsh and English, and a very capable surgeon. He was an extremely good person to have around in a crisis. He retired in 1993 having given 23 years of service to the Wrexham area.

Mr Joseph Hamlett.

Fetal Heart Monitors

By the late 1970s it was recognised fact that fetal distress could be apparent in some instances for quite some time, before it was picked up by visual or auditory means. Midwives, listening to the fetal heart, with a fetal heart stethoscope every half hour, could quite easily miss irregularities. If fetal distress was recognised early enough, the baby's delivery could be expedited, by delivering it by caesarean section or other means, thus giving the Special Care Baby Unit (SCBU) a better chance of saving the baby. At this time the Wrexham Maelor Maternity Unit did not have fetal heart monitoring machines and it

Newly qualified midwives who have just received their badges and hospital certificates, c.1985. Seated, 2nd row, L–R: -?-, Miss Megan Williams (Tutor), Mrs Eleanor Jones (Tutor), Mrs Myfanwy Povey (Senior Tutor), Miss Sexton (Director of Midwifery Services), -?-.

appeared that, as they were quite expensive to purchase, only the very large university hospitals had them. Our consultants approached the area health authority for funding, but were refused.

The Labour Ward midwives got together and discussed the advantages of having such a machine with the divisional midwifery nursing officer and it was decided that the Labour Ward staff should commence there own fund raising programme. 'Bric a brac,' arts and crafts, cake and clothing stalls were held by the midwives and nurses on their days off and brought in quite a bit of money. The clothes stalls were held in the Beast Market, with Wrexham Council waiving their rental fee. Dances, especially those held in Llay British Legion, increased the funds considerably for which our grateful thanks went to Mr Neville Rogers. When the local public got to hear about our efforts, the response was terrific, darts teams, football teams, quiz teams, scouts and many others helped. Patients and their relatives contributed generously to this fund, and eventually, we were able to purchase our very first Hewlett Packard fetal heart monitor.

The funds continued to come in and we were able, to purchases more monitors as well as drip counters which controlled the infusion rate of an intra-venous drip — these were much safer if we had a restless patient.

In July 1973, Mr Joseph D. Hamlett was appointed as consultant obstetrician and gynaecologist. He came from the Manchester area, and had worked at the Manchester St Mary's Hospital, and was a senior lecturer at Liverpool University prior to taking up his post at the Maelor Maternity Unit. He was a very academic person, and extremely conscientious regarding patient care. If he was worried about a patient, he would ring the hospital several times when he was off duty, to find out how she was, and it was not unusual to see him come into the unit at night. He started the first IVF clinic at Wrexham, with Sister Christine Gray, and gave lectures to the senior house officers and registrars, very

Mr Vlies wishes Sister Morgan well with her new post in Saudi Arabia.

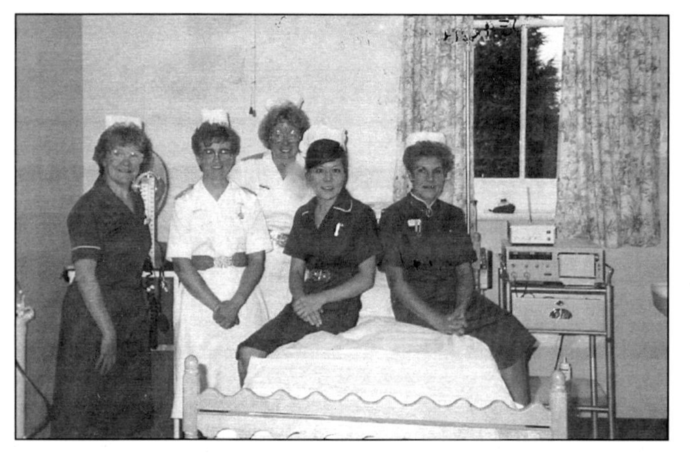

A group of labour ward staff in the labour suite, 1987. By this time, the indoor uniform had been abandoned in favour of one official uniform. L–R: Nursing Auxiliary Prue Jones, Staff Midwife Jill Bonsall, Staff Midwife Pritchard, Midwifery Sister Helen Bannister and Senior Midwife Joan Chaloner.

often using my office! They owe him a debt of gratitude for his help in getting them through their examinations. Sadly he became terminally ill in the early 1990s and when he died was only in his late 50s. He was very sadly missed and I personally learned a great deal from him, when I was studying for the Advanced Diploma of Midwifery.

In 1973 a new wing was added to the Maternity Unit, extending from the original entrance towards Maesgwyn Road. The ground floor ward was called Simpson Ward and the ward above it Lawson Tait. Simpson Ward became an ante natal ward under the charge of Sister Pat Bell and Lawson Tait Ward became a post natal ward under the charge of Sister Cecelia Roberts. Gilliatt Ward was changed to a temporary ante natal ward, and later became a second gynae ward, under Sister Gray. Bonney Ward and Annex were on the ground floor under the charge of Sister Judy Roberts. Strachan Ward, on the ground floor was extensively altered to become a new Labour Through Stay Area, containing eight labour suites, and a receiving room (which could double-up as a delivery room), a midwives station and other offices were added. This new up-to-date labour area was opened around November 1978 under the supervision of Mrs Joan Chaloner (Senior Midwife). The old labour wards on the first floor were converted into three isolation wards (with bathrooms) and were attached to Blairbell post natal ward, under the charge of Sister Iola Jones. The orchard was converted to a car park.

In 1977 Miss Cranfield (Principal Nursing Officer Midwifery) retired and was succeeded by Miss Mary Sexton, the job title changing to Divisional Nursing Officer Clwyd South. By the time Miss Sexton retired in 1988 the job title was Director of Midwifery Services Clwyd South.

1982 brought about the retirement of Mr David Barry Whitehouse, senior consultant obstetrician and gynaecologist, after 23 years on the staff of the hospital. He was a very quiet, shy person but, when you got to know him, the kindest person you could meet. His surgery was of an exceptional standard, and all house officers and registrars made a point of getting into theatre at sometime whilst he was operating, to learn from his technique, even if they were not on his team. Overseas doctors were extremely impressed with his surgery and he was a very good teacher.

Mr Robin Vlies was appointed consultant obstetrician and gynaecologist in 1982. He had been working as senior registrar in obstetrics and gynaecology at the Middlesex Hospital, under the Queen's obstetrician and gynaecologist, Mr George Pinker. At this time the obstetric and gynaecology demands of the area became greater and in February 1989 another obstetrician and gynaecologist, Mr Toon, was appointed, becoming the fourth consultant at the Maelor Maternity Unit.

In 1988 Miss Menna Williams transferred from St Asaph Hospital, to the Wrexham Maternity Unit as Director of Midwifery Services Clwyd, a post she held until her retirement in 1999 when Mrs Dawn Cooper was appointed Head of Midwifery and Women's Services Clwyd — again a new title.

The first phase of the new Ysbyty Maelor was completed in 1986 and in January 1987 the two gynaecological wards moved over to the new building. The Maternity Unit, however, did not move until 1999.

Wrexham Maelor Maternity Unit was renowned for its very high standard of midwifery care and expertise, mothers were allowed the choice of how they wished to have their normal deliveries carried out, a system which attracted many women from other areas of the country (e.g. Cheshire, Shropshire and Gwynedd) to Wrexham and, on a few occasions, doctors who had left the area would bring their wives back to Wrexham for the delivery of their babies.

Midwifery Tutors 1960–2002

Miss Mavis Hughes (Senior Midwifery Tutor)
Miss Laura Jones (Senior Midwifery Tutor)
Miss Myfanwy Jones (later Mrs Povey, Senior Midwifery Tutor), she retired as Senior Course Co-ordinator (Midwifery) her title having changed.
Mrs Eleanor Jones (Midwifery Tutor)
Miss Megan Williams (Midwifery Tutor)
Miss Celia O'Sulivan (Midwifery Tutor)

Paediatrics

In the1940s care of sick children in the Wrexham area was carried out by GPs and physicians. Children requiring hospitalisation were placed on adult wards and cared for by Dr John Forbes and Dr Philip Evans who had an interest in the care of sick children. Poorly children with heart conditions were transferred to either Myrtle Street Hospital, Liverpool, under the care of Professor Capon, or Alder Hey Hospital, Liverpool.

In 1950 Wrexham's first paediatrician — E. E. Gerald Roberts — was appointed, and from this time the care of sick children in the area took off. Dr Roberts' vision eventually came to fruition and enabled Wrexham to be in the forefront in developing holistic child health services for babies and children, offering in-patient and outpatient care and, in particular, care by the multi-disciplinary child development team which involved the community professionals.

Dr Gerald Roberts, BSc, MB, BCH, MRCS, FRCP, DCH.

When Dr Roberts first arrived he was introduced to his department which was in a two-storey building that was originally part of the Croesnewydd Workhouse, and had in the past housed sick and retarded children, and elderly and infirm inmates. The downstairs rooms had no properly constructed floors and there were spittoons everywhere. The place was in a generally poor condition. Eventually this building was upgraded and converted into two up-to-date children's wards and offices, and a children's unit with fifty beds was created. Hans Anderson, the upstairs ward, was for babies under the supervision of Sister Dodd. Lewis Carrol Ward was downstairs, for children up to the age of twelve years, under the supervision of Sister Pownall, and later Sister Williams. The main type of cases in the children's unit were those suffering from pneumonia, and gastroenteritis. Orthopaedic cases, ear nose and throat, and eyes, including surgical operations and accidents and emergency cases were cared for in the children's ward at the War Memorial Hospital.

In the 1950s there was a large outbreak of poliomyelitis in the Wrexham area and the isolation hospital had over twelve iron lungs in use at one time, stretching the medical and nursing staff to their limit.

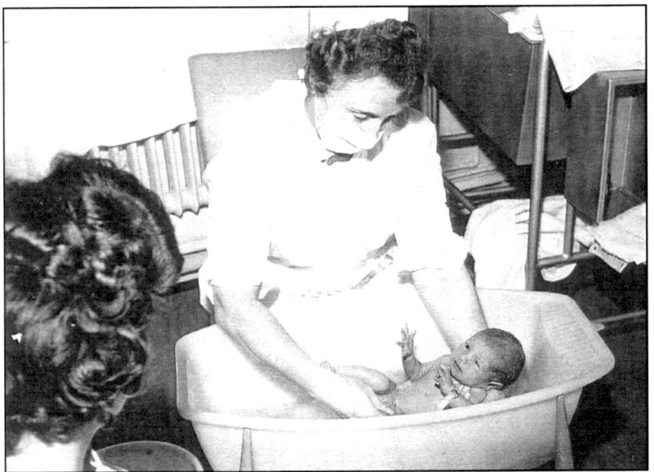

Bathing baby.

Dr Roberts held clinics in Wrexham, Chirk, Llangollen, Welshpool, Mold, Rhyl, Colwyn Bay and sometimes Dolgellau. Domiciliary visits also had to be carried out when requested by a GP to see a case in the home of the patient. He received £2 per visit. Sometimes, when the child required hospital admission, he would take mother and child back in his own car, a Ford Prefect, a vehicle that was well known to the public! In the early days parents were encouraged to visit in visiting hours only. This system eventually changed, and parents were allowed to stay with their children for as long as they wished, and were even put up in special parents' rooms at night. Dr Roberts retired in 1984.

Special Care Baby Unit (SCBU)

This unit was upgraded in the 1960s, with extra cots, incubators and modern technology. The improved care enabled many more pre-term infants to survive. From the early 1970s the unit was supervised by Sister Marian Williams.

In 1979 Dr Geraint Owen was appointed as a second paediatrician. Born and educated locally he was a very keen and efficient paediatrician, who was always up-to-date with new trends in paediatrics. A very caring, popular person.

In 1984 Dr Minchom was appointed as paediatrician. He was very popular with the children, always joking and making them laugh, both parents and staff thought a great deal of him. His clinical work was exceptional and he was always ready to teach new skills to medical and nursing staff.

1986 Dr Hywel Williams was appointed, and worked for a short time in the Wrexham Children's Centre but, because of commitments, returned to south Wales. and was replaced by Dr Brendan Harrington.

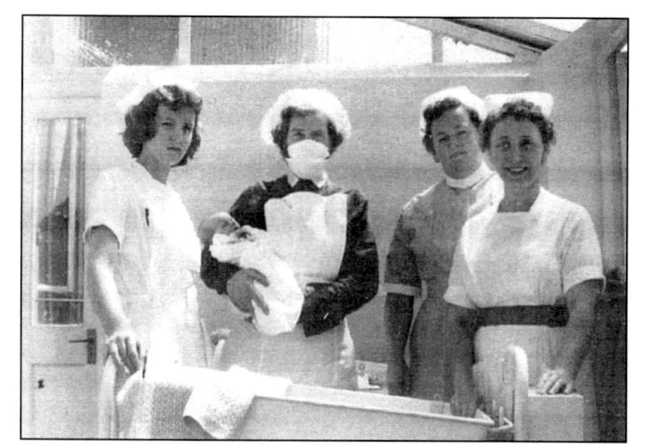

Sister Randles and staff at SCBU in the 1960s.

SCBU staff celebrate Christmas 1960s.

Sister Marian Williams, SCBU, c.1995.

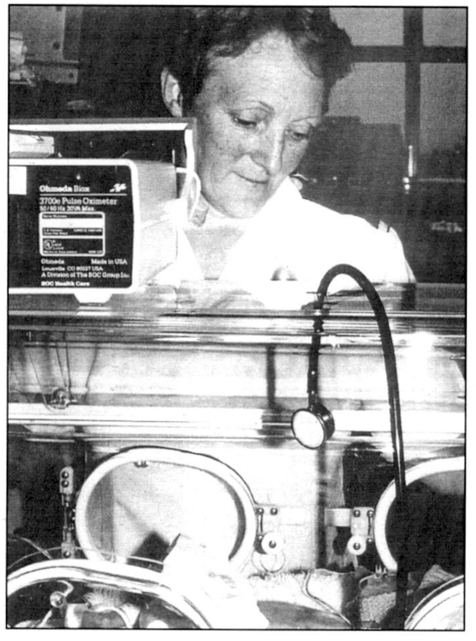

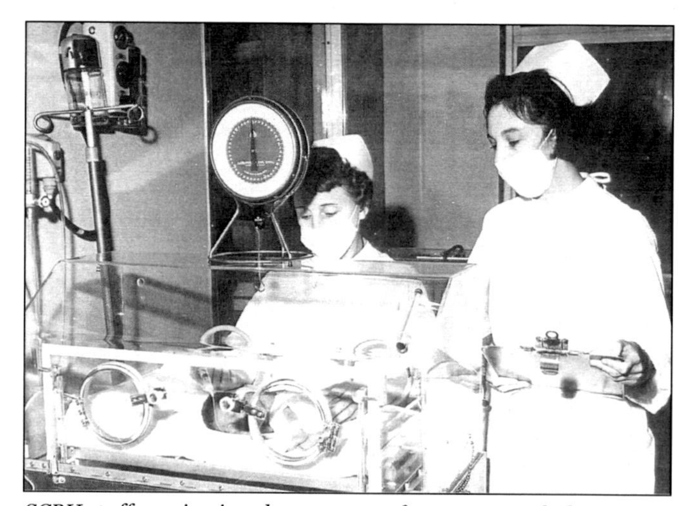

SCBU staff monitoring the progress of a premature baby.

Dr Sheila Harris, a paediatric clinical assistant, worked with the new born babies and children in Wrexham for many years. Her approach to children and child-care was unique. She never wore a white coat, because sometimes children became apprehensive, and related better to someone in casual dress. Her usual attire was a dress, or skirt and top, with a floral pinafore, for ward rounds and clinics. She was extremely kind to both patients and staff and always spoke in a quiet voice. Her clinical work was exceptional. She retired around 1990.

The Spastics Unit

Opened in 1960, this unit was situated on the right-hand side of the entrance gates leading from Maesgwyn Road to Croesnewydd Hospital. The Duchess of Gloucester visited the unit on the 17 November that same year. The first patients were taken from a ten mile radius of Wrexham — a population of 150,000. Fifteen were accepted for a trial period at the day centre, ranging in age from 2 years to 12 years, most of them having been treated at Wrexham, Gobowen, Birkenhead, Chester or Clatterbridge hospitals. An assessment panel observed the child's physical and mental handicap over a period of time after which a complete clinical evaluation was

Staff and children in the Spastics Unit.

carried out by the paediatrician, orthopaedic specialist, psychiatrist, county medical officer, speech therapist,and any other specialist that might be able to help in the individual case.

The unit was supervised by Sister Enid Jones, with a senior physiotherapist, an occupational therapist, a teacher, a speech therapist, two nursing aides, two cadets, voluntary workers and one domestic. The children attended the unit from 9.30am to 4.30pm Monday to Friday. Parents discussion groups were arranged, with a physiotherapist present, who would give guidance to parents to help with home management and exercise. In 1981 Sister Jones retired and Sister Geraldine Gilbert took over.

In about 1985 the children's wards were moved to the Maelor General Hospital complex and in 1998, after extensive alterations to the old children wards and a complete refurbishment, the Spastics Unit (now called the Child Development Centre) which had already amalgamated with the Maelor Children's Centre, moved in under the name of the Maelor Children's Centre.

Dr Gerald Roberts had introduced a new approach, not only for the care of sick children, but also to help and care for children in need within the community. The forgotten children included spastic children, Down's syndrome children and other mentally retarded children, including those who were being abused. It enabled the child community professionals to come together with the hospital professionals to all work together with the same aim in mind, giving the child their right to lead as normal and as qualitative a life as possible.

Illegitimate children

In the early part of the last century, it sometimes happened that when a family was poor and living in overcrowded conditions, a new born baby became an extra mouth to feed, a situation that was just impossible to accept. Some parents just gave the new-born away to another married couple, who were willing to bring up the child as their own. No legal documents were exchanged, and the baby was given the new parents surname, but the birth certificate was not altered. This happened to my husband's aunt. When she died in 1992, she was well into her eighties, and the family was unable to obtain a birth certificate because they were looking for the surname of the adoptive parents. It was eventually discovered that her birth was registered under the name of her blood parents.

In the late 1800s and early 1900s, those unfortunate unmarried girls or women who found themselves pregnant, and who had no parental support, were referred to public or charitable institutions such as the workhouse from where their babies were eventually sent to orphanages and other children's homes such as Barnardos. There was no policy or system for dealing with adoption. When children were put into care, it generally meant many years of institutional care, until they reached the current age of employment.

Later, towards the 1930s, private adoption by a third party was sometimes carried out with doctors, vicars, parish priests and matrons, who had knowledge and experience of the circumstances within their area, acting as the 'referring agents'. They often tried to place the baby within adoptive parents of the same religion as the mother. These adoptions were generally organised by solicitors where the case involved the pregnant daughters of middle and upper class families. Adoption rarely came into play for the lower social classes until the late 1930s. As late as the 1960s, wholly private adoptions seemed to be the legal policy.

One of my social worker associates informed me that over a period of five years in the 1960s he was involved in only one private adoption with a solicitor and client who initiated the matter herself. Later when he was a magistrate in the 1970s he was present for the making of adoption orders at the private juvenile court hearings. The only people present were the magistrates and the clerk, the social worker of the adoption agency (often a church children's society), the child to be adopted and the adoptive parents — the natural mother and putative father having already given their consents before other magistrates were not present. The adopters were invariably middle class married couples.

Today, all adoptions have to be carried out according to procedures specifically required by the law and supervised by the local authority's social services department. Magistrates are no longer involved.

Bersham Hall

Bersham Hall was opened by Denbighshire County Council as a home for unmarried mothers and babies, probably around 1946/7. Unmarried girls and women, who came here from various parts of the country, were admitted a few weeks before they were due to have their babies, and were given help and guidance in their preparation for childbirth. They delivered their babies at the Maelor Maternity Unit, and were discharged back to Bersham Hall, seven days post-natally, or ten days post-caesarean section.

Pregnant girls got to handle their friend's baby and a learning process began. Once the child was born, the girls cared for it under supervision — bathing, feeding and dealing with the baby's and their own personal laundry. They usually formed friendships with others there and helped one-another. The girls stayed at the home until the adoption of the

Bersham Hall.

Matron Ingram, Bersham Hall.

new-born was finalised.

During the adoption process, all mothers were given a period of six weeks when they were allowed to change their minds. All adoptions from Bersham Hall were dealt with by the Lancashire Adoption Society.

During the 1950s and 1960s, Matron Olive Ingram was in charge of Bersham Hall and her husband served as the care-taker. Matron Ingram was very well liked and respected by the girls at the home. She also served as the lady superintendent and sister tutor for the Wrexham British Red Cross.

Bersham Hall closed as a home for unmarried mothers and babies in about 1974.

Nazareth House

In 1937 Bishop McGrath appealed to the sisters of the Order of Nazareth to open a home to care for young orphaned children in Bala. There were a number of Roman Catholic people resident in this small town also, who were anxious to have a mass centre. The arrival of the Sisters of Nazareth at Bala was welcomed with delight, and the local Catholics gave unstinting help with the new home. A small Catholic church was built, and a nursery opened to care for young children. After about ten years, it was realised that there was a need for a bigger establishment and, as there was insufficient space for extension, a new home was sought. As Bishop Pettit wished the sisters to remain in the diocese, a larger home was purchased in Llanystumdwy, near Cricieth, and the sisters took up residence there in March 1949. Because the home was larger, they were able to accommodate more children, and the extra room allowed them to open up a separate area for the care of the elderly. Once again, local people helped the sisters with their work.

In the 1960s, it was once again recognised that there was a need for larger premises, and Hillbury House, Wrexham, the former home of the Bury and Crowe families, was purchase. The Sisters of Nazareth moved to Hillbury House, set in beautiful and spacious gardens in 1965, and work started on extending the establishment to accommodate a new nursery for infants, called 'Plas Maelor' and an unmarried mother and baby unit, called 'Plas Gwyn' (the name of the country house they had occupied at Llanystumdwy). Part of the new building, called 'St Joseph's Residential', was designed to accommodate and care for the elderly. All functioned under the collective name of 'Nazareth House'. The house was officially opened and blessed by Bishop Petit on 21 December 1966.

Above: Hillbury, the house that formed the basis of Nazareth House, with the new wing on the left.

Right: Sister Oliver (second from the left) and Sister Gertrude (third from the left) with other sisters in the grounds of Nazareth House.

Unmarried Mother and Baby Unit — Plas Gwyn

Unmarried girls and women, of mainly Roman Catholic religion, came from various parts of the country to have their babies at Nazareth House.Some of the babies were adopted by adoptive parents of the same religion, and those babies who were not, were looked after in the nurseries until school age when they were moved on to orphanages. All babies were baptised by the chaplain at Nazareth House. Local general practitioner, Dr Toby Ryan, gave supervisory care to the mothers and babies, the nursery children and the elderly.

An interesting story was related to the author. About twenty-eight years ago, a young 'gymslip-mum' came from the Coventry area to have her baby at Nazareth House. Her parents were extremely upset about the pregnancy and, when the girl delivered the baby, arrangements were made for her to be transported to Australia to live with relatives. When the baby girl was born, the young mother had photographs taken of herself and her baby, so that she could have them as a keepsake. It must have been a heart-breaking wrench to leave her baby behind. In due course, the baby girl was adopted, by a couple in the Cardiff area who had also adopted a little boy some two or three years earlier.

The baby grew up, with loving and supportive parents, had a good education, and eventually became a social worker. Knowing that she was adopted, she decided to try and trace her real parent or parents. This was unknown to the natural mother in Australia, who had never married, and who constantly thought about her baby, wondering how she had grown up, and where she could be. All she had were the photos taken at the birth. She contacted the Nazareth House Archives in Cardiff where her inquiry coincided with that of her daughter, who worked in Cardiff. Eventually they found one another, and the mother came over on a visit from Australia and arranged to bring her daughter to Nazareth House in Wrexham, to see where she was born, and to show her the delivery room, the photographs she had kept all those years, and, more importantly, to explain the reasons why she was unable to keep her. Mother and daughter have formed a close relationship, the mother having moved permanently from Australia to live in Cardiff to be near her daughter. The girl thinks no less of her adoptive parents, holding them in high regard, and still has a close relationship with them.

Around 1987, due to changes in the needs of society, the requirement for a mother and baby home declined, and this service was phased out, with the extra space then being utilised by the nursing home for the care of the elderly.

The Sisters of Nazareth were very sad that because of the decline in vocations, it became necessary for them to give up their work in what they described as the most beautiful part of north Wales and in April 2003, Nazareth House was taken over by a private nursing home and the name reverted to Hillbury. Over the last 66 years, over ninety sisters have worked in north Wales, and almost nine hundred patients have been accommodated and cared for.

Chapter 10

TUBERCULOSIS

The North Wales Sanatorium, Llangwyfan

In 1902/3 the Wrexham and district statistics stated that 10% of deaths by infectious diseases were caused by tuberculosis (previously known as phthisis). This lingering and infectious disease affected young adults in the early prime of life, and was found chiefly amongst the poorer families where there was overcrowding in the homes, lack of nourishing food and poor hygiene. In 1903/4 there were 57 deaths from the disease, and the MOH, Dr William Jones, stated that the disease had increased considerably. The Joint Fever Hospital did not cater for this type of disease.

Many people who had the disease were not always aware of it, thinking they had cold- or flu-like symptoms, and continued to work until they could work no more, at the same time innocently spreading the infection. The victims often ended up impoverished and under the care of the local workhouse. If the condition had been discovered earlier there may have been a chance of a cure. A law was introduced, that anyone caught spitting in a public place, like on the streets etc. would be fined £5 (which was quite a lot of money at that time) as spitting by an infectious person increased the spread of infection.

King Edward VII expressed deep concern regarding the health of some of his subjects who suffered from tuberculosis and, after his death, the King Edward VII Welsh National Memorial Association was formed in Wales. Members decided to locate a tuberculosis sanatorium at Talgarth in south Wales and Sir D. S. Davies, MP, purchased Plas Llangwyfan Farm in the vale of Clwyd and donated it to the King Edward VII Welsh National Memorial Association, in memory of his late father-in-law, Thomas Gee of Denbigh. This became the tuberculosis sanatorium for north Wales.

The Environmental Health Records Department 1913 Annual Report for Denbighshire recorded the following statistics of phthisis or pulmonary tuberculosis.

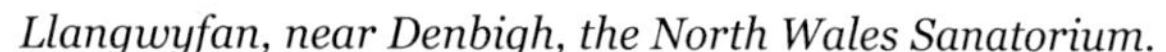

Llangwyfan, near Denbigh, the North Wales Sanatorium.

Two Llangwyfan nurses brave the cold to have their photograph taken.

N° of cases

9 below school age, 2 deaths
14 school age, 1 death
19 domestic servants, 4 deaths
4 colliers, 1 death
2 shop assistants, 0 deaths
2 railway employees, 0 deaths
1 school teacher, 0 deaths
1 shoemaker, 0 deaths
1 cabinet maker, 0 deaths
1 tailor, 1 death
1 leather worker, 1 death
1 brick moulder, 1 death
1 gardener, 0 deaths
1 carter, 0 deaths
4 others with no occupation, 0 deaths

Totals – 64 infected, 11 deaths

In the Wrexham area, upon receipt of notification of a case of tuberculosis (which was often called consumption by some of the general public) a visit was made to the home of the patient. A record was made of the general condition of the home — how many occupants, bedrooms, toilets and whether there was running water and sanitation. Printed information was given to the patient and householder about the disease and how to avoid contamination, backed up with verbal advice and guidance. In some cases, pocket spitting-flasks were supplied to the patient, and a supply of disinfectant, with instructions on how it was to be used. When the infected patient was moved from the room, or if there was a death, all belongings were disinfected and the room fumigated. This treatment was carried out by officials under the funding of the King Edward VII Welsh National Memorial Association which was represented in the Wrexham area by Dr E. L. Middleton, who had a dispensary in Temple Row, Wrexham. There was close co-operation between the dispensary and the public health department. Dispensary staff examined specimens of sputum and swabs etc. from all contacts.

The North Wales Sanatorium was opened at Llangwyfan in 1916, with 110 beds. Later many extensions were built, among them a 50-bedded children's ward, situated in the surgical block, to which Mrs Lewis the daughter of Sir D. S. Davies made a large contribution. On 16 July 1920 the North Wales Sanatorium was officially opened by King George V and Queen Mary but, as the disease was on the increase, there was a dreaded fear of it, and many objected to its location in their community and there was a limited response by the locals to help staff the hospital. As a result, many young people were recruited from south Wales and Ireland to serve as orderlies and nurses — some of them marrying local men and remaining in the area. After a while the

Llangwyfan cottages. Patients who were fully recovered were moved here and encouraged to become self-sufficient, preparing their own meals, doing their own laundry, shopping and attending social functions.

Hut 'D' male orthopaedic ward. Patients suffering from TB of the bone (e.g. Pott's Disease) were treated here. These patients are being treated on 'Gobowen' beds and may be hospitalised for a further two years.

Physician Superintendent Dr Biagi.

Matron Miss Blodwen Morris, 1954–70.

Above: Christmas dinner c.1957.

Hut 'C' with ward orderlies, domestic and student nurse Peter Wilson leaning on the bed.

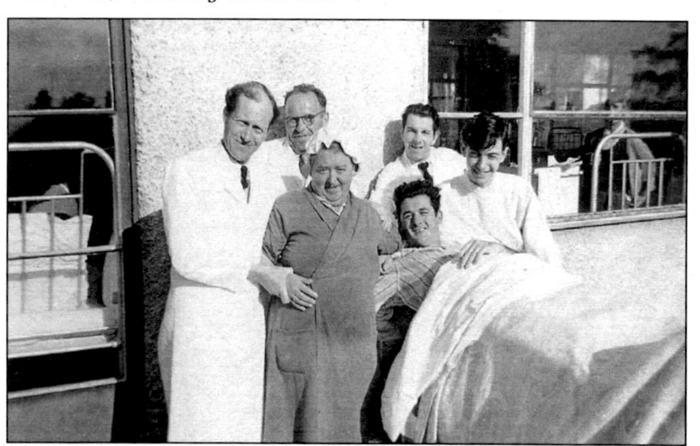

Christmas on the children's ward with nursing and medical staff.

local community began to accept the sanatorium in their area, although the fear of the disease remained for many years to come.

The great pioneer of thoracic surgery Mr Hugh Morriston Davies was appointed consultant thoracic surgeon at Llangwyfan in 1920.

By 1930 the hospital was accommodating 275 patients (including 50 children) and more land was purchased, and the bed capacity plus staff ratio increased. The period of stay for individual patients varied greatly during the 1930s and 1940s. Rest and fresh air was prescribed and a six months stay, was regarded as being relatively short. The doctors graded each patient's condition every week and when a patient had achieved a top grade it did not necessarily mean a discharge, sometimes it could mean that the patient was deemed to be in a fit condition to undergo surgery. During the early years, no ward or cubicle windows were fitted with glass, having 'louvre shutters' instead and it was 1936 before glass and heating were installed.

When Dr Hawkins arrived at the sanatorium in 1940, extensive improvements were carried out to all buildings.

There was an increase in male military patients admitted during the Second World War.

In 1952 the North Wales Sanatorium was re-named Llangwyfan Hospital.

Consultant surgeon Mr Ifor Lewis of the Royal Alex Hospital, Rhyl, who carried out surgery each week at Llangwyfan

Mr Peter Wilson's memories of Llangwyfan Hospital

Peter Wilson remembers applying for the post of student nurse at the sanatorium in 1956, when he travelled from mid Wales for an appointment with Matron, Miss Blodwen Morris, and the Sister Tutor, Miss Kate Williams. He recalls Miss Williams trying her best to put him off becoming a nurse, because of the high failure rate among male students. He was asked if it was his intention to take the state preliminary examinations, and hoping to please them said 'Yes' not realising at the time that he had agreed to take not only the B.T.A. training, but also to train as a State Registered Nurse. A strict medical examination was carried out by the medical officer, on all potential employees, with the Mantoux Test or the B.C.G. injections being given. In this particular 'set' there were only two students, Peter Wilson and Betty Evans, but there was usually four intake 'sets' each year.

Peter started his training on the 1 August of that same year, his first ward being Hut 'B' which was under the care of Charge Nurse Gallagher who initiated him in the making of the beds, 'Always smooth the creases Mr Wilson' he would say, and stressed the importance of keeping the ward tidy. As students they had to take turns in 'bumping' the floors, using a special type of polisher and creating a shine to gladden the heart of any sergeant-major. Before the 'bumping' of the floors, the ward maid would sprinkle damp tea-leaves, left from the breakfast tea-pots, over the floors, and then sweep them up in order to kept the dust down. No vacuum cleaners in those days!

After a few weeks in Hut 'B' he went into the classroom (the preliminary training school) where work started at 10am, Before this, the day started by reporting for duty to Hut 'A' at 7.30am, under the supervision of Sister Penn and Staff Nurse Morris. School work was under the tuition of Kate Williams, who instructed them in all aspects of hygiene and nursing care; they also visited the sewage works to see how things worked there. A visit was also made to a large dairy to see how pasteurisation of milk was carried out — a very important procedure in helping to reduce the causes of tuberculosis. Later, as they became more senior, they studied the different diseases that they were likely to nurse, and their care and specific treatment.

In the dining room different grades of staff were strictly segregated i.e. only staff of the same grade shared the same table. At the end of the meal everyone remained in their seats, until the home sister stood up to say grace, then everyone would leave the dinning-room in order of seniority. i.e. sisters in light blue uniform, then staff nurses in purple and students in grey striped uniform. Male students wore regulation blue-corded trousers and a shirt. Enrolled nurses were in green uniforms. Auxiliary nurses wore pink. Ward orderlies wore green.

All students had to reside in the hospital residence. On Saturdays everyone had to be in the residence by 11pm. If anyone wanted to be out later, they would have to obtain a pass from the matron. Of course, rules and regulations could always be overcome, usually a nurse with a room on the ground floor would let the revellers in, unknown to home sister. No one was allowed out after a late duty on week days (which was 8pm) the emphasis being on keeping staff healthy, because of their continual exposure t the infectious tuberculosis. Peter, however, did manage to go out to the pub, on one or two occasions after late duty, riding his 98cc autocycle. The following morning, he was sent for by matron who read the 'riot act'

A group of the porters at Llangwyfan, c.1960.

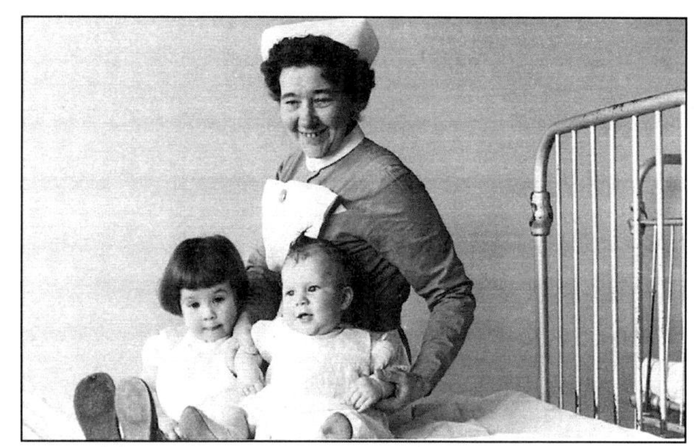

TB could attack any age group — staff nurse with two very young children.

Television and film actor Patrick Wymark visiting the children's wards at Llangwyfan.

Senior medical and nursing staff, 1960s. L–R: Home Sister Miss Coombes, Charge Nurse Gallagher, Miss Salt (hospital secretary), Matron Blodwen Morris, Dr Biagi (physician), Admin Sister Miss Moira Jones), Sister Hilda Williams, Asst Matron Miss Allerton.

Postcard of Llangwyfan Hospital, 1960s.

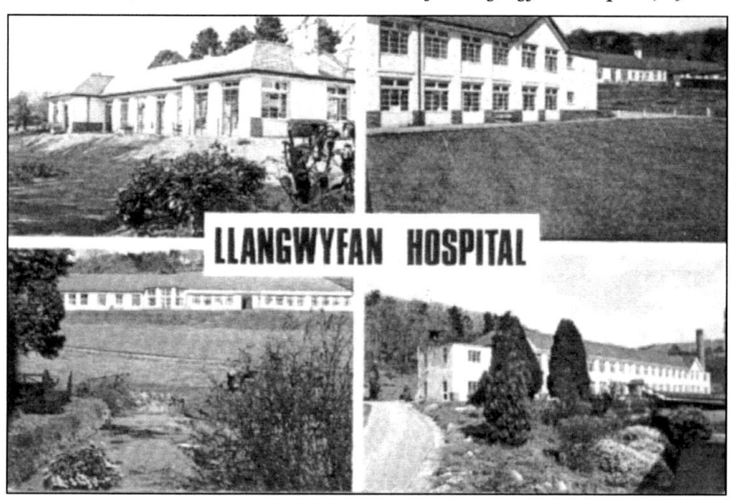

to him, because she had heard his bike coming in as late as 10 o'clock.

There were a few overseas doctors who also lived in the residences.

Dr Meyers, an elderly female doctor with a passion for croquet, often coerced the junior doctors and student Peter Wilson into a game. At the time, Peter was the only male student nurse at the hospital. Some of the visiting consultant surgeons were: Mr Ifor Lewis, Mr Hywel Hughes, Mr Hugh Reid, Mr Dickie Doyle (GU), Mr Norman Roberts (orthopaedics) and Mr Hugh Morriston Davies, a great pioneer of thoracic surgery. Some of the resident doctors were Dr Baigi, Dr Glyn Penrhyn Davies, Dr Mary Gallagher, Dr Mary Mayers and Dr Novak. There were also a succession of overseas doctors who came to Llangwyfan for cardio-thoracic experience.

The Kimmel Arms was the local pub for the 'Sani' staff. In the evenings they would walk across the fields, past the sewage works and then through Eddie Wynn's field. The licensee, was 'Pop' Pendleton, who often invited Peter to share his and his wife's supper, a favourite dish being tripe and onions.

Peter worked on all the different male wards:

> Hut 'D' — which catered for orthopaedic cases, with several patients suffering from Potts Disease (T.B. of spine). These unfortunate young males were placed in a plaster shell, made especially for them, which were mounted on wooden frames and put onto Gobowen Beds. The patients could remain like this for two years or more. Gobowen Beds were designed to allow the beds to be wheeled easily outdoors, or elsewhere, as the need arose, enabling patients to get plenty of fresh air and rest. Surprisingly these patients always remained cheerful, and were always up to tricks.
> Block 8 — a 50-bedded children's ward.
> Block 9 — where the theatres and x-ray departments were located.

Peter obtained his BTA Certificate after two and a half years, and then went on to train for State Registration at Clatterbridge Hospital. He later qualified as a psychiatric nurse, at the North Wales Psychiatric Hospital, Denbigh.

Sister Dorothy Ramsell's memories of Llangwyfan Hospital

Sister Ramsell did her general nurse training at the War Memorial Hospital, Wrexham, and, on qualification in 1954, she and the rest of her set thought they would remain there as staff nurses. The hospital had been their home for nearly four years, but a shock was to come! Matron Hague was very insistent that she and some of her colleagues were to go to Llangwyfan Hospital to train for their BTA (British Tuberculosis Association) certificate. It was quite possible that matron did not have posts available for the newly qualified nurses, but all she said was that there was a great shortage of BTA nurses, and advised them to take the training. She remembers they were all upset and crying. However, they went to their rooms and packed their belongings, and the following day, after saying good-bye to their friends, boarded a bus and travelled to Llangwyfan.

In great trepidation they arrived at the hospital on a Saturday morning, and were met by the home sister who gave them a lovely smile, and chatted away as she showed them to their rooms. The warmth and welcoming atmosphere relaxed them and allayed their fears somewhat. They were then individually interviewed by the matron who warmly welcomed them and, after asking various questions, went on to explain what training for the BTA certificate entailed. The rules of the hospital were strict, and because the patients they were going to nurse were suffering from the infectious disease tuberculosis, special precautions had to be taken, every nurse was encouraged to eat well, and get plenty of rest, to maintain their immunity levels. The girls took an instant liking to matron, and felt much happier. They were told to report to the sister tutor in the classroom on the Monday morning.

They really loved working at Llangwyfan Hospital and took an instant interest in the various tubercular conditions, their treatment and trained with enthusiasm. The food they received was exceptionally good, and the care and attention given to them was very much appreciated. Later, they made friends with the people of Llangwyfan and went regularly to the weekly dances and other entertainment, including the local pub. Needless to say they were all successful in passing their exams and were awarded their BTA certificate. Most of them continued working at the sanatorium for some time afterwards. Sister Ramsell met her husband at Llangwyfan, he was an army officer who was a patient at the hospital.

During the 1960s the number of tuberculosis cases reduced dramatically, due to the introduction of intra-muscular streptomycin — staff administrating this drug had to 'gown-up' and wear masks and surgical gloves to prevent them developing an immunity to the drug. isoniazid and para-aminosalicylic acid were given orally. This chemotherapy revolutionised the treatment of all forms of tuberculosis and the majority of acute, severe forms of the disease, such as military TB, were now cured and most patients survived.

Llangwyfan Hospital eventually changed to a hospital for the care of the elderly and chronic sick patients before closing in 1980. Plans for the hospital to become a village complex for the care of people with special needs were never implemented.

The Wrexham Chest Clinic

This clinic, located at 18 Grosvenor Road, Wrexham (officially called the King Edward VII Welsh National Memorial Tuberculosis Institute) was possibly opened around 1946/7, and replaced a dispensary that had been situated in Temple Row. Various chest complaints were dealt with at the clinic including sarcoidosis, bronchiectasis and asthma, to name a few. But in the earlier years the major complaint dealt with was tuberculosis.

Dr Clifford Jones, a very caring, kind and very efficient person, was the consultant chest physician. He always read his own x-rays, but if there was a problem with diagnosis, would seek a second opinion from Dr Stanley Nowell, the chief radiologist, who was based at the War Memorial Hospital. Dr Jones retired in 1975 and Dr Baker took over the clinic.

In the 1950s and 1960s Sister Mansell was the sister in charge, with responsibility for a very well run clinic, giving follow-up Mantoux tests and BCG vaccinations She was a kind, very active person, with the ability to put patients at their ease.

Mrs Marion Lloyd Jones was the chest clinic health visitor, who followed up with the community care of patients and contacts with tuberculosis.

Pamela Williams was the radiographer, who was a very capable efficient person, always friendly and cheerful, and again someone who could allay the fears of the patient. (which was very important when dealing with patients with tuberculosis.

Out patients clinics continued to be held in various parts of north Wales, as well as in Grosvenor Road, Wrexham. Later the Grosvenor Road clinic closed and Dr Baker moved his clinics to the War Memorial and the Maelor Hospitals,and continued his visits to clinics in the various outlying hospitals, in the region. In 1986 the Wrexham chest clinics were moved to the new Ysbyty Maelor, still under the care of Dr Baker.

Dr E. Clifford Jones, consultant chest physician.

Chapter 11

Palliative Care

Macmillan Cancer Relief

In 1911, a young man called Douglas Macmillan witnessed his father suffer from cancer, his needless pain and his eventual death, made him take up the cause to plea to the public to facilitate help for cancer sufferers, where anyone in the country suffering from cancer, could have equal and ready access to the best information, treatment and care. He made out the case for the availability of nursing homes which would give care and attention either free or at a low cost. He envisaged 'a panel of voluntary nurses' available to tend the needs of cancer patients in their own homes. In 1911 the Society for the Prevention and Relief of Cancer was established.

In 1924 the charity became a benevolent society and was renamed The National Society for Cancer Relief. In 1930, the first fully-paid member of staff was appointed and, four years later, the first local committee for cancer relief was formed in Bath. The first flag day also took place in that same year, in Swindon, Aberdare, Barry, Penarth and Cardiff.

By 1969 the charity was allowed to support in-patient care and make its first contribution to the building of hospices. In 1975 the first Macmillan nurses were funded and the charity built its first Macmillan Cancer Care Unit. £2.5 million was invested in 1980, to expand the Macmillan nursing teams throughout the UK and in 1993, HRH The Prince of Wales funded the 1,000th Macmillan nurse. Eventually, in the late 1990s, the charity changed its name to Macmillan Cancer Relief which today supports people suffering from cancer throughout the UK. It can offer financial help to people on low income and give expert care, with practical and emotional support, which makes a real difference for those people living with cancer. All Macmillan nurses are senior SRNs, with specialist training in cancer care, working within the NHS. The charity sets up posts for Macmillan nurses with a three year grant, after which the NHS takes over the funding.

Above: Mrs Hilda Roger.

The Wrexham Macmillan Nursing Service started in the early 1980s with one Macmillan nurse in post, Mrs Hilda Rogers, a trained general nurse and midwife, who had been nursing twenty years when she read about the national hospice movement, and she felt that her true vocation lay there. She helped Dr Graham Arthurs bring palliative care to Wrexham in the early 1980s. Macmillan nurses developed and increased their services over the years, and in 2002, became part of the Macmillan Specialist Palliative Care Team, working and liaising with hospital and community nursing and medical staff, providing information, advice and support to cancer patients and their families. At this time terminally ill patients were cared for in their own homes, as this was the recommended way for their care.

Nightingale Ward at the Maelor Hospital was used as a day care and support ward where patients were helped to cope with their illness, both mentally and spiritually, and were given pain relief. Nightingale Ward was closed when the purpose built Nightingale House Hospice was built in 1995.

Just before she retired, Hilda Rogers gained the degree of Batchelor of Philosophy and Nursing Studies. After her retirement, she lectured on palliative care to nurses at the University of Wales, Bangor and in the Wrexham and Glan Clwyd hospitals. During this time she had the privilege of meeting HRH Prince Charles, when he

Right: Mrs Hazel King.

opened a new hospital wing at Llandudno Hospital. Sadly, she herself became terminally ill and died in April 2004, aged 61 years, with one of the Macmillan nurses she had trained at her bedside.

One of the longest serving Macmillan nurse in Wrexham was Hazel King, who came to the Wrexham area in 1987 and worked tirelessly to help and support both her patients and her colleagues. She had a vision for better care for people suffering with cancer, and it was through her energy and determination, that the Cancer Drop-in Day Centre (The Fight Cancer Together Club) was formed in Chirk in 1998. Hazel retired in 1999, after being diagnosed with cancer, and sadly died in 2001. She was a dedicated nurse, working with enthusiasm and foresight, and is greatly missed.

Marie Curie staff, 1999.

Marie Curie Cancer Care

The charity, the Marie Curie Memorial Foundation, was founded in 1948 and named after the Polish-born scientist, Marie Curie, (1867–1934) who discovered radium. She won two Nobel prizes in recognition of her contribution to science. The Foundation joined with the Queen's Nursing Institute to carry out a survey of 7,000 patients who had cancer and were being nursed at home and the ensuing report was published in 1952, highlighting four areas of need. As a result of this the first Marie Curie Nursing Home was opened in Cupa, Scotland, followed by the Marie Curie Nursing Service which was established in 1958, to provide day and night care for cancer patients. In 1986 the charity changed its name to Marie Curie Cancer Care, adopting the daffodil as its logo, a symbol of hope in the continuing fight against cancer. The Wrexham Marie Curie Nursing Service is based at Tŷ Mawddach, Ysbyty Maelor, Wrexham where the district nurse liaison officer is Mrs Mair Hughes who provides a link between the hospital and the community, and whose nursing team supports and carries out nursing care of the patients.

Nightingale House Hospice

Nightingale House Hospice was the brainchild of anaesthetist Dr Graham Arthurs, who developed a keen interest in the relief of pain in the early 1970s. The 'Pain Society' had recently been formed which Dr Arthurs decided to join. He visited a couple of hospices in Oxford and London, which were essentially cancer hospices, which gave him 'food for thought'. He moved to Wrexham in 1978, having been appointed a consultant anaesthetist at the Maelor Hospital, and also set up clinics for chronic pain relief at the War Memorial Hospital. At the clinic the relief of chronic pain was dealt with by a variety of means, such as drug therapy, injections, nerve blocks, tens, acupuncture, relaxation, etc. Dr Arthurs chose to help cancer patients who had no real support at this time. When Dr Cole, of Christies Hospital, Manchester, the visiting radiotherapist at the War Memorial Hospital, was leaving to take up a position at St Anne's, the idea of a hospice in Wrexham was first aired. A fund was set up, called the Terminal Care Fund, designed to help the terminally ill patients and their families. It was well

The architectural award-winning Nightingale House Hospice, opened 6 November 1995.

Staff and day care patients in the lounge at Nightingale House.

supported, not least by the Fund's trustees, and in 1982 two Macmillan nurses were acquired and Nightingale Ward became available at the Maelor Hospital, which was used as a day support centre.

By 1983/4, four people were being employed and Nightingale ward became a focus of support and in 1989 there was a change in the NHS policy which meant that trusts could buy in services and it was agreed that, if enough money as raised, efforts would be made to set up a new hospice in Wrexham. The Clwyd Area Health Authority, agreed to support some of the running costs, and, in 1990/91, a board of trustees was set up, under the chairmanship of Mr Mervyn Phillips, who was overseer of this ambitious project.

A suitable site was found at Plas yn Llwyn, the old nurses home, on Chester Road and money began to come in from numerous personal grants and donations. The hospice building was designed by TACP, and there was tremendous support from the former Archbishop of Wales, Dr Alwyn Rice-Jones, who was the original president of the Terminal Care Fund.

The Nightingale House Hospice opened its doors on 6 November 1995 and was officially opened by the Duchess of Gloucester in June 1996. Mrs Linda Johnson became the first matron. She retired in 2004 and was succeeded by Mrs Tracy Livingstone.

Above: Dr Graham Arthurs receives a cheque in support of the Nightingale Terminal Care Fund from the hospital staff who put on an Old Tyme Variety Show in the 1970s.

Right: A group of nurses and carers outside Nightingale House.

Nightingale House Hospice promotions and management team with the Mayor and Mayoress of Wrexham, Cllr and Mrs Neil Rogers.

Chapter 12

Personalities

Dr John Forbes

Chief Consultant Physician, Wrexham War Memorial Hospital

Dr Forbes was born in Ryton-on-Tyne, County Durham, and is remembered as being a caring gentleman and a talented artist and gardener. He came to the War Memorial Hospital in 1947, and dedicated 30 years service to the community. He served as chairman of the Society of Physicians in Wales, was president of the North Wales Branch of the British Medical Association, and was a member of a great many other medical committees. During his long career, he was a regular contributor to the editorial columns of the *British Medical Journal*, as well as author of a number of papers and medical books, including co-authoring the widely read textbook, *The Clinical Examination of Patients,* with his life long friend Willie Mann, who was physician to the Queen. Doctor Forbes retired in 1977, and died on 1 February 2003, aged 90 years.

Mr John Eber Spalding, FRCS, MS (1907–64)

Consultant surgeon, Wrexham War Memorial Hospital

John Spalding, the son of a Royal Navy surgeon, was born in Hong Kong and brought up and educated in Ramsgate, Kent. He entered Guy's Medical School in 1929 and, after qualification, he later became a surgical registrar at Guy's and demonstrator on anatomy and an examiner in surgery for the General Nursing Council (GNC).

During the Second World War he was a surgeon at the Emergency Military Services Hospital, (EMS) in Farnborough, where he 'patched up' many a pilot.

In 1946 he was the first consultant surgeon to be appointed at the Wrexham War Memorial Hospital, and possibly the only Master of Surgery ever to be appointed to a Wrexham hospital. Working at the War Memorial Hospital and the Maelor Hospital he was also visiting surgeon to Welshpool and Dolgellau hospitals.

A very quiet, conscientious and gentle person, his surgery was exceptional. His wife remembers, that when they went away somewhere for the weekend, he always had to be back by Sunday late noon, so that he could carry out a ward round and familiarise himself with the patients he would be operating on the following day.

He was author of several medical papers, and in the early 1950s wrote a paper on 'Early Ambulation Post Operatively, to prevent Deep Vein Thrombosis' which resulted in radical changes in surgical post-operative care being made across the country.

Mr Spalding died on 9 December 1964, at the young age of 57 years. In September 1967 a medical library in was opened in his memory, situated near the Maelor Hospital pathology department. In 1990, a new, purpose-built, John Spalding Library, was opened by HRH Prince Charles, Prince of Wales at the Medical Institute, Croesnewydd Road, Wrexham.

1959

Robert Ninian says farewell to Matron Hammond on his retirement day.

Mr Robert Sheddon Ninian

Consultant surgeon, Maelor General Hospital

Mr Robert Ninian came to Wrexham in 1941 as the first surgeon in charge of the new Emergency Military Services Hospital. He was born in Rutherglen, Scotland, and obtained his FRCS (Edinburgh) in 1935. After the Second World War, he went to serve with the BAOR (British Army of the Rhine) Medical Service as a major from 1947 to 1949 and then returned to Wrexham, where he became medical administrator at the Maelor General Hospital.

Mr Ninian was president of the Welsh Association of Surgeons, the Wrexham Clinical Society and the Medico-Legal Society, which he helped to found. He served on the Wrexham, Powys & Mawddach Hospital Management Committee, and was a chairman of the Medical Staff Advisory Committee.

He was a person who commanded respect and his surgery was impeccable, a style which he taught to his subordinates. Nursing students we were in awe of him, ward sisters held him in very high esteem and when it was the morning of his ward round, everywhere had to be cleaned to perfection. On the trolley the patients' case notes, with x-rays and path lab reports were put in order ready for the round during which he had a large retinue of people with him i.e. registrar, house officers, secretary and physiotherapist. We could hear the steel tips on his heels quite clearly as he came down the long main corridor. Ward nursing staff were lined up on either side of the ward corridor and he would 'sweep through' the swing doors that a junior nurse held open in readiness for him, and his entourage. He would greet the sister with politeness, and maybe crack a joke with her as they entered the ward. He would cross question his medical staff regarding the treatment and investigations of each patient's condition, or the curtains were pulled around a bed so that he could examine a patient's wound, and he would tell patients when they could go home.

As the medical administrator he attended all Hospital Management Committees, along with other surgeons, physicians, specialists, councillors and matron, and had a large say in how the hospital finances were spent. He kept his finger on the pulse of the hospital and would know if even a drain was not working properly — oh, to have this system of management back again!

Mr Ninian retired early due to ill health, and died at the age of 57 years.

Mr Martin Linsey Smith

Consultant surgeon, Maelor General Hospital

Mr Smith was the second consultant surgeon to be appointed to the Maelor Hospital in succession to Mr Ninian. He originated from the Manchester area and worked in Wrexham from the 1950s until the early 1970s. He was an extremely clever person, capable of carrying out brilliant surgery, but he did border on eccentricity, and did not carry the commanding aura of Mr Ninian. He was friendly and liked a joke, and would speak to any grade of staff. One evening when I was a junior student nurse, I took a patient to theatre who needed an emergency appendicectomy. Mr Smith was 'on call' and was waiting in theatre when we arrived. I knew he worked very quickly and could carry out an appendicectomy in three minutes flat and therefore the theatre nurses had also to be quick. In those days, the ward nurse had to stay in theatre and act as the non-sterile nurse so I 'gowned-up' and put on a mask and over shoes. As the non-sterile nurse I tied the gowns of both Mr Smith and the theatre sister, and carried on helping the other theatre nurse.

The operation was almost complete, and Mr Smith was putting in the last of the sutures, when his theatre trousers fell down to the floor — although his gown was long and covered most of him, his underpants could be seen! He turned round and glared at me, saying, that it was my fault because I had unfastened his trousers when I tied his gown. My eyes nearly popped out of my head, I knew I had done no such thing, then I could see the sister and the other nurse laughing, an knew he was teasing. He completed his suturing, with his trousers around his ankles!

He usually cycled to and from the hospital and his home. When he was on call and had to come in to the hospital in the evening, or at night, he would ride his bicycle to the ward down the long Maelor Hospital corridor. On one occasion, when I was on night duty, I was on my way to theatre to collect a patient for the ward, when I saw Mr Smith cycling along the corridor away from me, towards one of the female surgical wards. He propped his bike against the corridor wall, and walked through the swing doors into the ward. Before I had reached the theatre, I saw a nurse peer through the door that Mr Smith had gone through; she was looking to see if there was anyone of 'importance' on the corridor, the next thing she was joined by someone else, and they were doing something to his bike. About ten minutes later my patient was ready to leave theatre for the ward and, as the theatre porter and myself wheeled the trolley out onto the corridor, we heard loud expletives, coming from lower down the corridor. The nurses, who were nowhere to be seen, had fastened every unmentionable to Mr Smith's bicycle, and he obviously could not remove them. The next minute he came cycling past us heading for the entrance hall where the porters were stationed, seeking their assistance. He looked so comical, we could not stop laughing as we passed the entrance hall!

Alf Jones (left) with porter Gwyn Evans by the War Memorial boiler room.

Alf Jones

From hospital porter to E.C.G. technician

Alf Jones started working at the War Memorial Hospital in 1944 as junior porter. His main duties were to travel by carrier bicycle to Croesnewydd Infirmary and the Emergency Military Hospital to collect specimens for the Pathology Laboratory at the War Memorial Hospital, and take their results back when ready. This carrier bicycle could always be seen parked outside the door of the front hall of the War Memorial Hospital, when not in use. It was quite often the case that on a Sunday morning the bicycle would be missing and it would be found later in the day, by a local policeman in Llay, Rhosrobin, Rhos, etc. having been stolen by a person who had been drinking, and had missed the last bus home. The bike was sometimes found damaged and, on its return, would be taken to Walter Roberts' shop for repair.

When Alf attained eighteen years of age he became a porter and his main duties were to aid the mortuary attendant; when not doing this, he carried out general porter duties. He worked in the mortuary for six years or more. Matron Hague always took an interest in him, and one day saw him up a ladder on one of the out buildings. She opened the corridor door, and called out to him 'Is that your work?' and when he replied 'No, Matron'. She said 'Well jolly well get down then'.

Around 1956, Matron Hague approached Alf and asked him if he might be interested in taking a course to become an ECG technician. He said he was interested and in due course arrangements were made for him to attend Liverpool Royal Hospital, where a training course was being held. He travelled daily, and completed the course after two years and was appointed ECG technician for the Wrexham Powys & Mawddach Hospital Management Board, and attended both Wrexham hospitals, plus outlying hospitals, from Dolgellau to Welshpool. He also held a regular clinic in the Robert Jones & Agnes Hunt Orthopaedic Hospital in Gobowen.

When consultant surgeon Mr Ron Todd arrived as a new surgeon in Wrexham, around 1965, he asked that a different technique be used for ECGs to be carried out in theatre. Alf then had to attend Manchester Royal Hospital to familiarise himself with this technique, and a different machine was obtained.

Towards the late 1960s Alf left the NHS and was employed at British Steel.

Hadyn Hughes, BEM

Porter, Wrexham War Memorial Hospital and Maelor General Hospital

Hadyn Hughes originated from Bala, but lived for most of his life in Rhos, near Wrexham. He married Kathleen who worked for many years, until her retirement, in the doctor's quarters at the Maelor Hospital.

In 1962, Hadyn started to work as a porter in both the War Memorial and the Maelor Hospitals. For a period he worked in the Central Sterilisation Department (C.S.S.D.) as a driver, before becoming a theatre porter at the Maelor General Hospital. He later attended a course at the Mabel Fletcher College, and became a qualified theatre technician. Enthusiastic about his job, he decided to advance his education by studying and passing five O level subjects. Later, he attended Bangor University on a day release basis, and was successful in obtaining his theatre technician's diploma.

Hadyn was a very popular person who cracked jokes with doctors, nurses and patients, and had a brilliant personality. Most of all he loved working with children, always allaying their fears when taking them to theatre; he even created a 'Thomas the Tank Engine' theatre trolley, to transport the little ones making an adventure of what could be a very worrying journey. In 1990 a mother who had witnessed Hadyn talking to her young daughter before she went to theatre. He told her he would be back for her, with the 'Thomas the Tank Engine' to take her for a ride. He returned with the trolley decorated just like 'Thomas' with a train driver's hat for her to wear, and the flags, he made the right engine noises while she drove the trolley, making the whole experience fun. As a consequence, she had no unpleasant memories of her hospital stay. This mother was so impressed that she wrote to the Marje Proops 'My Extra Special Man' column in the *Daily Mirror full* of praise for Hadyn. The following year Hadyn was awarded the British Empire Medal, in recognition of his dedication and the very special manner which he had when dealing with patients, relatives or colleagues.

Sadly, after a period of illness, Hadyn died in 1992. The Chief Executive of the Maelor Hospital, keen to create a lasting reminder of this popular member of staff, recognised that many other members of staff had similar qualities as Hadyn, and that their commitment and dedication was also worthy of recognition, and so 'The Hadyn Hughes Award' was launched in 1995. This has proved extremely popular and recognises any person who, whilst working within the NHS, has made an exceptional contribution to the well-being of patients and/or staff through their caring and considerate approach. The award is still ongoing.

Porter Haydn Hughes sitting astride 'Thomas the Tank Engine', poses for a photograph with ENT staff and colleagues.

Chapter 13

Other Hospitals and Units

Brynkynallt Cottage Hospital, Chirk

Lady Rosamund Trevor (Countess of Bantree) was the second wife of Baron Arthur William Hill Trevor of Brynkynallt. They were married in 1897 and lost their only child, a five-year old daughter, in 1904. Brynkynallt Cottage, part of the Brynkynallt estate, was empty in 1898 and Lady Trevor allowed Nurse Booker, a district nurse for the area, to live at the cottage for five years. In 1905, when Nurse Booker left the area, Lady Trevor decided to convert the cottage into a cottage hospital for children and it functioned as such for the following twelve years very efficiently with the Trevor family meeting its running costs. Parents who could afford to do so, would contribute some small amount when they could. Two full-time nurses were employed — one as a home nurse, and the other as a district nurse — as well as two nurse-maids and two orderlies.

Records show that, in 1906, children were provided with some formal education, but we are unsure by whom — possibly by Lady Trevor herself or a member of the clergy. The maintenance costs of the building, replacement linen and the children's clothing were met by Lord Trevor.

Stables were built to accommodate donkeys which were used to carry coal and other commodities in panniers — donkeys were a cheaper commodity to buy and keep, their purchase cost being around £2 compared to the cost of a cart-horse which was anything from £35 upwards. A full-time gardener was appointed to the staff who was expected to supplement food to the hospital kitchen. Lord Trevor gave a yearly gift of over £40 pounds worth of coal to the hospital. Local doctors who attended patients at the Cottage Hospital charged a nominal fee of £2 or £3 per year.

In 1908 the hospital began to cater for adults and small donations were made by local organisations, supplemented in 1913 by the proceeds of a collection box in the surgery at Chirk. Brynkynallt and Black Park Collieries each made an annual payment of £10, thus starting a tradition of help for the hospital and a little later Mr W. T. Craig (owner of Brynkynallt Colliery) gave £10 towards the expenses of the adult ward. Ifton Colliery miners also contributed.

The 1914–18 war brought about changes. Although Brynkynallt Hospital was offered to the War Office in 1914, it was only taken over in 1916/17 to help cope with the great increase in war casualties. Extra accommodation was found for the wartime hospital by incorporating the Drill Hall in Station Avenue as an annex. Lady Trevor took up the administration of what was called the Brynkynallt Auxiliary Hospital, and was appointed commandant, while Dr Charles Salt was the medical officer-in-charge. The hospital was run by the British Red Cross Society and was closed in 1919. According to the 1918 accounts, Lord Trevor was responsible for the upkeep of both the 'cottage' section of the hospital and the sick and injured soldiers section, costing him over £700. In 1919, the Drill Hall annex was closed due to the demobilisation scheme,and most of their surplus equipment was distributed to the district nursing associations, the hospital in Wrexham and quite a lot was saved for the proposed new Chirk Cottage Hospital, and left in the care of Dr Lloyd.

Chirk & District Cottage Hospital

It was the ambition of Dr Lloyd to see the establishment of a fully equipped cottage hospital in Chirk, capable of dealing with the industrial and residential needs of the area. This ambition had been partly realised through the generosity of Lady Trevor, whose cottage hospital at Brynkynallt was for some years of invaluable benefit to the neighbourhood.

During the 1914–18 War, when Brynkynallt Cottage Hospital was under the control of the War Office the residents of Chirk made use of the Llangollen Cottage Hospital. After the Armistice, Dr Lloyd and his partner Dr Charles Salt, put forward their ideas of the type of cottage hospital which was required for Chirk. The plans were submitted to the Priory for Wales of the Order of St John of Jerusalem whose joint finance committee took the scheme on board. The British Red Cross Society immediately made a grant of £4,000, on condition that the people of the area contributed the same

Staff and patients at Brynkinallt Military Hospital, 1914–18. [Dr Marchant]

Staff and patients at Brynkinallt Military Hospital, 1914–18. Photograph taken on the site of the present-day ambulance station. [Dr Marchant]

Nurses at Brynkinallt Military Hospital, 1914–18. [Dr Marchant]

Chirk Hospital Staff, c.1930. Seated L–R: Dr Cuddington, Dr Charles Salt, Matron Morris, Dr Thompson, Dr Berresford. Back row: Miss Cooper (physiotherapist, wearing a 'butterfly' cap).

Chirk & district Cottage Hospital. [Neville Hurdsman]

amount, that five beds should be at the disposal of ex-soldiers, and that the society should have two representatives on the board of management. The Order of St John made a further grant of £2,500 with a condition that the people of the area contribute an equal amount. This was done and the building with all its equipment was completed.

Chirk Hospital was opened on the 11 August 1921 by Sir Napier Burnett and the first patient was admitted on 15 August. The building in addition to male, female and children's and private wards, had a fully equipped x-ray room, an operating theatre and an out-patients department (with two consulting rooms and one waiting room) approached via a separate entrance. The hospital was centrally heated.

In 1933 a further £3,000 was spent on alterations and additions to the hospital including an enlargement of the theatre and anaesthetic room, and improvements to the x-ray department, out-patients department, massage and electric therapy departments. A separate maternity wing was also added, with improvements made to the staff accommodation.

In the early 1930s Sir Beckweth Whitehouse, who had been knighted for his good work in the field of obstetrics and gynaecology, came from one of the large hospitals in Birmingham, at the invitation of Dr Salt, one or two Sundays a month, to carry out elective caesarean sections and other gynaecological operations. These caesarean sections must have been among the first to be carried out under general anaesthetic in this area of north Wales (Dr Salt often acting as the anaesthetist).

It is said that when Dr Salt's son, Pat, was a child of four or five years of age, he fell from the rafters of an out-building and sustained a compressed fracture of the skull (when a piece of the skull bone is pressing inwards onto brain tissue). There were no neurologists in those days and Sir Beckweth Whitehouse discussed the case with a very eminent surgeon named Samson who worked in one of the large Birmingham hospitals. As a result of this conversation, Samson came to Chirk Hospital, with his own anaesthetist and theatre nurse, and operated on the child, removing a small portion of skull bone which was pressing on the brain tissue. The child made a full recovery and followed his father into the medical profession dedicating his life to the care of the people of Chirk, working as a local general practitioner and in the Cottage Hospital. After this, Mr Samson came once or twice a month, on a Sunday, to carry out surgery at Chirk Hospital.

In 1935, Mr Robert Owen Jones was appointed County Consultant Obstetrician and Gynaecologist. The area he covered extended far beyond the county as far as Welshpool and Dolgellau. There was now no longer any need for Sir Beckweth Whitehouse's services. In 1959 Mr Robert Owen Jones retired, and Sir Beckweth Whitehouse's son, Mr David Barry Whitehouse, took over the appointment. He was an extremely skilled surgeon, with a quiet shy personality and great charm. He carried out over 1,000 operations at Chirk Hospital.

Dr Marchant acted as Mr Whitehouse's anaesthetist, and worked as a full time anaesthetist in the Wrexham hospitals. Being a resident of Chirk, he found Chirk Hospital very convenient and he was able to carry out daily post-operative care on the Chirk patients.

Until 1948 there was a public voluntary contribution scheme from the residents of the area, which helped with the up-keep of the hospital. Every class of worker was encouraged to make a contribution. The miners contributed a great deal of money, it being deducted directly from their wages by the works management. Others subscribed weekly, paying their money to a collector. A fully paid up member, together with his wife and children (up to the age of sixteen years) was eligible for free hospital care. Persons insured under the the National Health scheme made a subscription of ten shillings a year and were provided with similar benefits.

Chirk Community Hospital.

In the 1936 the hospital dealt with: 391 in-patients, 1,145 out-patients, 180 surgical operations, 432 x-rays, 62 maternity cases, 74 accidents and 18 dental care patients.

In 1948 the hospital came under care of the National Health Service, under the management of the local hospital management board.

In 1983 due to the re-organisation of the maternity services, it was deemed that the safest place for a mother to deliver her baby was in the larger type of maternity units, where the expertise of the medical and midwifery staff was available with all the modern technology, laboratory and theatre facilities, as well as a special care neo-natal unit. The delivery of new born babies ceased at Chirk, and the local mothers were delivered at the Maelor Maternity Unit. Primigravidae patients (patients having their first baby) were transferred to Chirk Hospital seven days post delivery. Multigravidae patients were transferred 48 hours post delivery. Caesarean births were transferred after seven days post delivery. Home confinements were rare.

In 1987 Chirk Hospital closed down to allow the building to be demolished and replaced by a new, purpose-built, community hospital.

In the 1930s, Matron Morris was in charge of the hospital. She was followed by: Miss Margaret Edwards, Miss Barlow, (covering Chirk and Llangollen), Miss Dilys Davies (1970s), Miss Ann Hill (1980s), Mrs Shirley Davies (1990s).

Llangollen Cottage Hospital

Warrington solicitor William Wagstaff made a considerable amount of money from to his involvement with early railway projects, and bought Vivod Hall in Llangollen in 1872. The following year his wife died and he purchased a piece of land on what was called the 'Jenny Jones' site in November 1875 where he built a hospital for the town of Llangollen dedicated to her memory. A memorial plaque, dedicated to Mrs Wagsaff, can be seen in the hospital today. It is said that there is a clause in the deeds of the Llangollen Cottage Hospital which states that, should the building cease to function as a hospital, it will revert to the 'Best Estate' (The Wagstaff's daughter married Mr J. C. Best).

After meetings with the Llangollen Urban District Council (UDC) and supporters of the scheme, it was decided that the hospital should be run from voluntary contributions. Amongst the hospital rules were:

> all subscriptions be paid yearly in advance on 1 January.
> the hospital should be run by a committee consisting of Mr Wagstaff, two members of the UDC and two representatives of the subscribers. The committee was later increased to three UDC members, and three representatives of the subscribers.
> neither infectious, nor chronic diseases, when considered incurable shall be admitted, nor such cases as are likely to require a very long and expensive course of treatment.

Chairmen

- Mr W. Wagstaff 1875–77
- Mr J. C. Best 1877–1907
- Mr W. Best 1907–48

Treasurers

- Mr W. Richards 1875–99
- Mr C. W. Richards 1899–1927
- Mr S. O. Richards 1927–48

The staff at the Hospital consisted of:

Matron — Miss Parlett who was engage at a salary of £30 p.a. This salary was later increased by £2-5-0 per quarter as porter money (porter was dark brown bitter beer, brewed from charred or brown malt). After a few months porter was supplied by the cask for the patients and staff, and the porter money was withdrawn.
Maid — who had a wage of five shillings a week.
Doctors — Dr Hughes, Dr Drinkwater and Dr Jones.

Llangollen Cottage Hospital.

The Annual Report, 1878, showed the cost per patient, per day, to be 2/8½ (14p)which was giving the committee some concern. Economies were introduced on butchers and coal bills, and the average cost dropped to 2/2¼ (11p) a day. There was no gas or electricity, and the cost of lamp oil for the first year was £2-2s.-9d. Other costs were:

Wine and porter was £21-3s.-5d.
Coals and wood, £55-18s.-½d.
Washing and charring, £6-17s.-5d.
Butcher, £55-18s.-½d.
Milk, £11-12s.- 8d.
Butter, £10-17s.-2d.
Grocer, £30-10s.-3d.
Repairs, £20-13s.-10d.

The system of one penny a week subscriptions was introduced at the opening of the hospital and continued until the National Health Service took over in 1948. Everyone who paid subscriptions had a card which was marked to show each weekly or monthly payment. This helped with the up-keep of the hospital and entitled the subscriber to free admission in cases of accident, or sickness of the type that could be cared for at Llangollen Hospital. The husband, wife and children(the latter not less than 8 years of age and not having left elementary school). The weekly payments could be made through the husband's employers, money being deducted out of their wages, or directly to the treasure of the hospital management committee. Other money to help with the up-keep of the hospital was obtained from all chapels (14) and churches (2) in the area. There were also alms boxes at the hospital and in local hotels. The hospital grew its own garden produce. Gifts to the hospital were numerous e.g. a bath-chair, and three nightingale caps; *The Graphic*, and a set of draughts; hares, pheasants, and rabbits; garden produce; old linen; various mineral waters. In the early days there were several a reports of shortage of water and a hand pump had to be installed in the basement. On 13 April 1876 the first patients were admitted to the hospital.

Patients Statistics for the first month in 1877:
The original trustees were – W. Best, W. G. Dodd and S. C. Richards.

Total number of patients, 41 (four being under treatment since previous year)
Deaths, 2
Discharged, 29
Relieved (recovered or improved), 3
Transferred to Shrewsbury Hospital, 2
Unable to cure, 5

1884, the hospital was extended and an extra ward was added on each floor and in 1925, a new wing was added to the building.

Patient Statistics, 1937

General accidents, 48
Road accidents, 10
Confinements, 13
Newborns, 11
Transfers, 5 (to Chester Hospital, Croesnewydd Hospital, Manchester Hospital and Gobowen Hospital)
Deaths, 5
Out-patients, 88

In 1958 a new out-patients department was added. In the late 1970s the hospital ceased to cater for maternity cases. In 1981 the hospital closed for a short period of time for the building to be up-dated with regard fire regulations and the labour wards were altered to cater for general patients,

The Matrons

1937, Miss Harris
1940s–1960s, Miss Price
1960s–1972, Miss Barlow, who covered Chirk and Llangollen Hospitals
1970s–mid 1980s, Miss Dilys Davies, who covered Chirk and Llangollen Hospitals
Mid 1980s–*c.*2000, Mrs Shirley Davies

Doctors

In 1937 the doctors were: Dr F. A. Drinkwater, Dr R. Drinkwater, Dr H. G. Morris.
Mr Jack Adam Davies came to Llangollen Hospital in 1955, and also worked as a general practitioner in the area, taking a keen interest in the obstetric side of patient care, with Mr Robert Owen Jones being the over-all County Obstetrician and Gynaecologist. Dr Davies was affectionately called Dr Jack, and to his friends, 'Jack Cold Hands', a character who was extremely well liked by colleagues, friends and patients. He retired in 1985. His father, Mr Richard Davies, better known as 'Dickie Dai' lived in Wrexham and was a member of the management board of the War Memorial Hospital, a very popular, well-liked gentleman. Doctor Jack's son, Dr Rhys Davies, has followed in his father's footsteps, continuing the family trend by being a local general practitioner and working at the Llangollen Cottage Hospital.

Ruabon Hospital

In November 1869 the *Wrexham Advertizer* published that Sir Watkin, and Lady Williams Wynn were 'desirous of promoting the establishment of a hospital in the parish of Ruabon, because of the large numbers of accidents which were occurring at the large collieries, and iron works, in the region.' They felt that such an institution was necessary as there was a population of over 14,000. Sir Watkin invited the local clergy, business proprietors and doctors to Wynnstay Hall to help set up this venture. A large number of gentlemen responded to his request and the baronet offered to erect a suitable building, the plans of which were submitted to the gentlemen that were present. The doctors present, offered their services services free of charge, and the clergy and others undertook to provide any assistance they could to bring the scheme to fruition.

By January 1870 the promoters of the 'Ruabon Accident Hospital' were able to open a temporary establishment in the house of Mr John Parry (the Old Grammar School building). Donations amounting to £140,000 had been promised in annual subscriptions and Drs Burton and Roberts had agreed give their services. Lady Williams Wynn promised to provide a portion of furniture for the hospital. Later that same year an 'Accident and Treatment Hospital' was built by the Wynnstay Estate, and opened on the site where the new library stands today. Drs Jones, Roberts, Davies and Turner, and others, carried out many operations and gave patient care there.

With the opening of the new War Memorial Hospital in Wrexham in 1926, accompanied by a decline in the coal industry, the need for an accident hospital at Ruabon declined and the Ruabon Hospital was converted into a temporary county maternity hospital in August 1935.

Penley Hospital

Originally built during the Second World War as a military hospital for the American forces. After the war these premises were vacated by the Americans and handed over to the 2nd Polish Corps of the British 8th Army and the staff and patients of a hospital in Senigalia were transferred to this site. Many other locations around Britain were used for the same purpose.

Penley Polish Hospital

Medical staff of the 3rd Polish Hospital, Senigalia, on the Adriatic coast, 1946. L–R: Dr Cogan, Dr Katzner, Mr Laczynski (pharmacist), Dr Brandt, Dr Berger.

3rd Polish Hospital, Penley, 1962.

A group of Penley nurses, c.1952.

A group of Polish patients at Penley, c.1962.

Members of the medical and nursing staff, Penley, c.1969.

Father Kaminski, a patient at Penley, who was a former inmate of Dachau concentration camp in Bavaria, in the chapel at Penley Hospital, c.1980.

Penley, was a 750-bed hospital which was equipped for the treatment of the wounded Polish soldiers who later became part of the Polish Resettlement Corps. The hospital was staffed mostly by Polish nationals, assisted by a few British staff. It is estimated that in the years immediately following the Second World War, Penley Hospital had a population of 2,500 and it became a village within a village. Over 2,000 children were born there, who were naturally Polish speaking, and Flintshire Education Committee set up a nursery school, allowing Polish speaking children to attend from the age of 3 to 5 years, after which their knowledge of English enabled them to attend the local primary school.

The hospital was split up into two sections, one half for the general patients, and the other for patients suffering from tuberculosis (the latter accommodated in eight wards). The boundary between the two was marked by the stream which runs through the land. In the late 1950s the TB section was closed, the majority of the patients having recovered from the disease, due to the introduction of new drug therapy.

At Penley, there were all kinds of work shops (e.g. for carpentry, shoe repairing and weaving) as well as a cinema, a snooker room, instruction in archery for the disabled and football.

Retirement party, Penley Hospital, 1978 for Staff Nurse Doryn and Staff Nurse Jagielska. As the Polish nursing staff grew older and retired, they were replaced by trained staff from the Wrexham hospitals.. Standing L–R: Mrs Moorhouse (Nursing Officer), Sister Szenderowicz, Sister Piggott, Miss Savage (Nursing Officer) and Mrs Pat Williams (Senior Nursing Officer).

The scale of the Polish Hospital at Penley can be judged from this aerial photograph taken in 1984.

In 1961 Penley Hospital, took on a new role, becoming a geriatric long-stay hospital for the elderly, chronic sick Polish ex-combatants and their families, and was transferred from the direct administration of the Ministry of Health to the Welsh Hospital Board under the care of the Wrexham Powys and Mawddach Hospital Management Committee.

The patients in Penley came from all walks of life, including a prince, known to the staff as 'Mr John', he was a member of one of the higher ruling families of pre-war Poland. One patient was a Roman Catholic bishop who had been in a Siberian concentration camp. Another patient was a priest who was arrested six weeks after joining the Polish Navy, and spent the rest of the war in Dachau concentration camp. There were also former Polish military personnel, majors, captains and colonels, as well as ordinary soldiers. These men had a common bond — none of them could return to a free Poland for which they had fought.

As the Polish staff grew older and retired, they were replaced by British staff. Monoglot English-speaking staff found communication difficult at first, but they soon overcame these problems by learning a few key words in Polish, and they developed a unique 'only to Penley' pidgin Polish!

Chapter 14

VOLUNTARY ORGANISATIONS

The British Red Cross Society

This was formed in 1870 when war broke out between France and Prussia. Lord Wantage, VC, wrote to *The Times* calling for a national society to be formed in Britain following the example of other European nations (initially inspired by a Swiss businessman Henry Dunant). In August 1870 a public meeting was held in London, and a resolution was passed that a national society be formed in this country (based upon upon the rules laid down by the Geneva Convention of 1864) to aid sick and wounded soldiers in time of war. The British National Society for Aid to the Sick and Wounded in War was formed which, in 1905 was reconstituted as the British Red Cross Society, and granted a Royal Charter by Queen Alexandra, who became its first President.

Skilled volunteers were required to prepare it for its wartime roll and a Voluntary Aid Scheme was introduced in 1909, to ensure that Voluntary Aid Detachments were formed in every county in Britain to provide aid to the Territorial Forces medical units in times of war. When war broke out 1914 the British Red Cross Society, in co-operation with the Order of St John, were organised into Voluntary Aid Detachments (VADs). All members were trained in first aid and some undertook training in nursing, cookery, hygiene and sanitation. The VADs worked throughout the war in hospitals, convalescent homes, rest stations, packing centres, medical supplies and work-parties, both at home and abroad. They provided the first motorised ambulances to the battlefields and established 'Message and Tracing Services' which sent

Wrexham Red Cross Society (Denbigh 6), mid 1940s, St Mary's RC Cathedral grounds. Front row L–R: D. Brookfield Davies, Mrs Ormrod (Transport Officer), Mrs Hampson (Asst QM), Dr L. Morris (Asst Cmdt), Lady Lowther (Dep. President), Mrs J. Duncan Robertson (Commandant), Dr Glyn Evans (MO), Mrs Kirby (Lady Superintendent), Mrs Horton (Asst QM), Mrs S. Bowen (Cadet Officer). 2nd row: Mrs Durwood (section Ldr), Miss Redrop, Mrs Seaton (Head Section Ldr), Mrs D. M. Thomas (Section Ldr), Miss Marjorie Williams, Mrs Hughes, Mrs Musgrave, Miss Massey Williams, Mrs M. E. Jones, Miss Ruscoe (Section Ldr), Miss Mary Lloyd, Miss M. Roberts (Asst Cadet Officer). Third row: Mrs Whitley, Miss V. Lewis, Miss M. Turner, Miss E. Thomas, Mrs W. Baker, Miss D. Melhuish (Sect Ldr), Mrs Smith.

Wrexham Red Cross Society

Wrexham Red Cross Society Cadet Detachment, 1945.

Wrexham Red Cross Society annual church parade, c.1948.

Wrexham Red Cross Society annual church parade, c.1948, marching to Gresford Church.

Wrexham Red Cross Society (Denbigh 6 & Denbigh 500) being inspected by Major General. L. A. Hawes after their parade at Ruthin, late 1950s.

An American, left-hand drive, Chevrolet ambulance donated to the Wrexham Red Cross Society and the Wrexham St John's Ambulance by the American Red Cross.

searchers out to areas where fighting had taken place to record the injured or dead soldiers.

In 1921, the British Red Cross established the first blood transfusion service in the UK and, in 1929, following the signing of the Third Geneva Convention the society established comprehensive rules for the treatment of prisoners of war.

During the Second World War, the role played by the British Red Cross Society (again in conjunction with the Order of St John) was similar to that of the First World War with members working in hospitals, convalescent homes, nurseries, ambulance units, rest stations and supply depots, providing nursing and welfare support. They also sent out standard food parcels, invalid parcels, medical supplies, educational books and recreational material, providing relief to displaced persons, especially those who found themselves in the hands of the enemy or an occupying power.

The British Red Cross worked hard to provide relief to victims of disasters, floods, earthquakes, including helping of refugees from the Hungarian Revolution 1956, the Vietnam War, famines in Africa, hurricanes and many other man-made and natural disasters. Within the UK, relief work followed disasters such as the collapse of the coal tip in Aberfan in 1966, the Lockerbie air disaster of 1988, and the 1998 Easter flooding, have been undertaken. The British Red Cross' main aim was, and still is, to focus on the improvement of health, the prevention of disease, and the mitigation of suffering throughout the world.

Wrexham British Red Cross Society

The Wrexham Branch of the British Red Cross Society started in 1930, and was part of the Denbighshire Branch with its headquarters in Grove Road, Wrexham. The Senior Detachment was designated Denbigh 6 and was followed by a Youth detachment (Denbigh 500) in the 1940s and a Cadet Detachment (Denbigh 3558) in 1944/5 (the latter with its original HQ at Pendine Hall, Stansty). All members were given instruction in first aid, home nursing, hygiene and the application of various types of bandages, splints, slings, etc.

Lectures were given by Drs Glyn Evans, Barry and senior members of the Red Cross, and the various individuals were examined in those same subjects. Success in the more advanced type of examination, allowed the successful candidate to be promoted within the organisation. Miss Martha Roberts, a school teacher, and member of the Red Cross, remembers quite clearly, during the war years being taken with a group of Red Cross nurses to Borras Airfield to be instructed in rescuing airmen from a crashed aircraft.

Inter-county competitions were held throughout the country. Mock situations were set up e.g. a road traffic accident, an air or train crash or a person having fallen in the street. Teams from each county, under the control of a team leader, were required to attended to the victims and apply their skills. Examiners marked each team on their ability and expertise, the team with the highest marks winning the trophy.

Wrexham's Blood Transfusion Service

Wrexham British Red Cross set up the first Blood Transfusion Service in the Wrexham area, during the war years. Panels of donors were organised made up of people who were willing to give blood as the need arose. Blood was taken from the donor, in what were sometimes called 'Bleed Sessions' at the War Memorial Hospital and later, as the technique became more proficient, at places of work e.g. factories and collieries.

Dr L. Morris of the Red Cross, and Red Cross nurses who had received some

Mrs Winifred Baker (Denbigh 6) who worked at the War Memorial Hospital during the Second World War and carried out other Red Cross duties including blood donor sessions.

training in this field, carried out the work. Some of the Red Cross nurses were qualified nurses, and were an asset for this type of work. Other local doctors (GPs) became involved and the service became invaluable.

Wrexham Red Cross (Denbigh 6). A group of members pose outside their First Aid tent at the Llangollen International Eisteddfod in the 1960s.

Hospital Duty

Many Red Cross nurses worked at the local hospital and cottage hospitals during the war and during the 1950s. In the Wrexham area, their work was purely voluntary. The author's mother, Winifred Baker, did her nurse training at Hope Hospital, Salford, in the early 1930s, and worked at the War Memorial Hospital, in the theatre, casualty department and various wards. She was awarded medals for her war work and other achievements.

The Youth Detachment, Denbigh 500

Started in the early 1940s at Grove Road, Wrexham.Young ladies attended this section between the ages of 18 and 25 years. The commandant was school teacher Miss Brookfield-Davies.The assistant commandant was Dr L. Morris. The usual Red Cross training was carried out with examinations taken in the various subjects. The Youth Detachment also competed in the different county youth competitions. When appearing on public duty they, and the cadets, until they became proficient, were always accompanied by an experienced senior Red Cross nurse.

The Youth Detachment also carried out hospital work. Apart from nursing there was the hospital trolley shop, where members took the trolley around the wards, and patients bought whatever they required. If any patients did not have visitors, a note would be made and the Red Cross would ensure these patients were visited by members on a regular basis. When, for whatever reason, a patient was unable to write their own letters, these young ladies would do so on their behalf.

Parcel Distribution

Mrs Bagnall-Berry of the Red Cross was in charge of parcel distribution. She worked very closely with hospital almoners, and welfare departments. Food parcels were distributed to the needy elderly and the disabled in the Wrexham area.

Wrexham Red Cross Society Cadet Detachment (Denbigh 3558), Pendine Hall, 1944/5.

These people were not only extremely grateful for the parcel but were also often thrilled to have a visitor,to whom they could chat about local news.

The Red Cross also gave 'comforts' to any retired or disabled prisoners of war. Many parcels were sent from this area to our soldiers who were being held in prisoner of war camps.

Escort Duties

Red Cross nurses would escort patients from their homes to hospital for treatment, or from the hospital to their homes on discharge

Loans

The Red Cross Society, loaned out medical requisites to people who were being nursed in their homes, i.e. air-rings, special mattresses, commodes, etc, to help make life more comfortable, and allow the patient to stay in their own home environment.

Other duties carried out by the Red Cross Society

A duty rota would be made out for Red Cross members to attend duty at the various Wrexham cinemas — the Majestic, the Odeon, the Hippodrome, the Glynn and the Empire as well as football matches, fetes, carnivals, church parades, inspections, the annual Llangollen International Eisteddfod and Bangor Races. During the Second World War, some of the American forces were based at a camp in the village of Penley, and other places, and these young men came to town to visit the cinemas, public houses, and to generally enjoy themselves. The Wrexham Red Cross, set up a café at the bottom of High Street, for the Americans. It appeared to be a cellar room under a shop, where Parry's the saddlers and Downs & Roberts confectionery shops were situated. In this little café, affectionately called the 'Doughnut Dugout', Red Cross members cooked doughnuts, and made expresso-type coffee, which was milky and very enjoyable. They also sold Coca- cola all of which was quite foreign to the Wrexhamites! It was a very popular little café with the Americans, and would hold approximately 40–50 people, and was always crowded.

Wrexham Red Cross Cadets, Denbigh Detachment 3558

The cadet officer was school teacher Miss Bowen and the assistant cadet officer Miss Martha Roberts, who was also a school teacher. The cadet detachment started in 1944/5 at Pendine Hall, Highfield, Stansty. At this time, the hall had been taken over by a group of young ladies aged between 11 and 18 years who had been evacuated from a remand home in Croydon, the home being run by nuns, with a matron in charge. There was strict discipline, but all the girls were well cared for. The girls attended Brynteg School, and walked to school in crocodile fashion, through the hamlet of Highfield, down into Poolmouth Valley (later to be called Moss Valley) and up the other side into Brynteg. The journey was carried out twice daily, because they came back home to lunch.

The author was one of the first members to attend the Cadets, and although I was slightly under age I was accepted. Three other girls who were 14 years of age were also accepted from the village. The girls from the 'Home' made up the rest of the cadet numbers. Eventually other girls from the Wrexham area joined. We were taught first aid, home nursing and hygiene, and there were practical sessions of bandaging, application of splints, the use of the many-tailed bandages and slings. I became adept in the application of the capelline head bandage, which was an intricate procedure, and not bad for a nine-year old. We were taught how to care for the unconscious patient, the treatment of over-doses, burns, scalds and many more situations, all of which were of great benefit to me when I later took my nurse training. The girls I associated with were always kind and friendly, although some of the older girls were rather 'street-wise'. I struck up a friendship with a little girl of 11 years, and could not understand at the time why she could not come to my home, until my mother explained the reason to me. At Christmas there was festivity and jollity and restrictions were relaxed somewhat.

Pendine Hall, Highfield, Stansty.

Everyone, was given a Christmas present, including the outsiders, and I was 'over the moon' with mine especially because it was given to me by my little friend.

Red Cross cadets were encouraged to help on children's wards and with the elderly, in both hospitals and nursing homes, where they helped make beds, give out meals and, in some instances, fed a helpless patient.

St John's Ambulance Association

The St John's Ambulance Association was originally formed in 1877, its primary function being to instruct members of the public in first aid and other allied subjects. The Association was the non-uniformed, or the teaching branch. It was some ten years later that the St John's Ambulance Brigade was formed, being the uniformed, or operational, branch of the St John's Ambulance Foundation of the Order of St John. The two branches worked closely together.

The Wrexham St John's Ambulance Service was inaugurated in 1927 by the Chief Constable of the Denbighshire Constabulary, Mr George Guest. This came about as a result of travelling to Bangor-is-y-coed in his car, he came across a serious road traffic accident. He stopped his car, and went to the aid of the victim. Having had first aid training, he did what he could to help, but was most put out when he discovered that there was no official ambulance service in the Wrexham area. After commandeering a lorry, he travelled on the back of the vehicle with the patient to the Wrexham Hospital. After this experience he set to work to form the Wrexham Division of the St John's Ambulance Brigade. Many men joined this worthwhile cause, mainly railway workers and miners, and lots of people contributed to the cost of Wrexham's first ambulance, via collection boxes and donations.

All St John's Ambulance members were trained to a very high standard in first aid and care of the sick. The service was completely voluntary maintained by one annual flag day and public donations. Men would work a full shift at their employment and, on arriving home, would wash and change, have a meal, and then present themselves at the ambulance station for duty. A duty rota having been worked out in advance. At weekends some ambulance members would take it in turns to be on night duty at the station, which was a hut in the yard of the Wrexham Police and County Buildings (now the Wrexham Museum). All ambulance calls were relayed to the police station where was a large bell near the switchboard. If a call was a non-emergency, the telephone operator would press the bell once, and press three times for an emergency. This bell could be heard clearly in the ambulance hut.

Ambulance personnel were encouraged to take their driving test as soon as possible, a great many did so at the age of 17 or 18 years of age. Gradually as time went by, the Wrexham St John's Ambulance Brigade boasted the ownership of three Bedford ambulances and one Austin ambulance car. All vehicles were mechanically maintained by Camps Garage, Vicarage Hill, Wrexham. During the Second World War, more ambulances were obtained and the American Red Cross made a donation of left-hand drive Chevrolet ambulance to Wrexham in 1943/4.

Dr Glyn Evans did sterling work as a teacher and promoter of first aid and the care of the sick. He gave lectures to the St John's members and acted as an examiner. After successfully passing advanced examinations, individual members would be allowed promotion if deemed suitable.

In 1946, the first fully paid St John's ambulance driver/operator was employed — St John's member Mr Walter Clutton. Following him came, Gwilym Smith, Glyn Jones, Dave Stace and others.

Prior to 1946/8 all fatalities were taken to the War Memorial Hospital to certify death, before being taken to the mortuary, a building near to the Ruabon Road Cemetery where victims were then washed and laid-out respectably by the ambulance personnel. Again, everyone needs to be reminded that these people were still working in a voluntary capacity.

Wrexham Football Club welcomed

Wrexham St John's Ambulance, 1927.

Wrexham St John's Ambulance, 1932.

Wrexham St John's Ambulance, 1937.

Wrexham St John's Ambulancemen.

Wrexham St John's Ambulance, with their ambulance, 1950s.

Above: Members of the Wrexham St John's Ambulance pose alongside a new Land Rover ambulance, presented by Miss Kathie Dougall and committee members of the Wrexham Variety Club in 1979.

Wrexham St John's Ambulance taking part in Mayor's Sunday, 1964. The detachment is marching past Guildhall Square on Chester Street.

the St John's Ambulance members to all their matches. They attended injuries to footballers as well as any problems with spectators. This was where a lot of experience was obtained, and the football authorities would donate a cheque to the St John's Ambulance Fund. Of course, footballers in those days did not get the huge salaries, that are given today — they were lucky if they got £8 per week.

Cadets
The St John's Ambulance Brigade Cadets were started in 1932. They were encouraged to join between the ages of 11 and 17 years. These boys were instructed in the elements of first aid and the care of the sick, and took examinations accordingly.

Cadets were always accompanied by an adult St John's member when they were out and about, as practical experience was far greater than theory.

Harry Down's memories of the St John's Ambulance Cadet Force.
Harry Down vividly remembers joining the Wrexham St John's Ambulance Brigade Cadets in 1932 when Bill Morris was Cadet Supervisor. They had their headquarters in a cellar under Astons Furniture Works in a room called the 'Joy Centre', situated between Salop Road and Willow Road. At the top of this building was a dance hall with a maple floor. After a few years the cadets moved to another small building, belonging to Soames Breweries, where lemonade was produced.

Harry attended Grove Park Grammar School and, until he had been issued with his St John's uniform, would go on duty in full school uniform, plus cap, and his St John's bag over his shoulder.

When Bangor Races were on, he was always a willing volunteer for duty. At the races their were strict rules and regulations, two St John's members were to man each jump, in case of falls. Quite often they had to walk a considerable way to the jumps, up to three or four miles, there were no 4x4s or radios in those days. If the ground was soft and boggy chains were wrapped around the ambulance wheels so that they could get a grip. Not only did they have to walk a long distance to the jumps, they had to carry blankets under their arms and a large satchel containing dressings, bandages and various sized splints. They also carried flags on poles. If there was a fall at a jump, they would raise a white flag if an ambulance was required and a red and white checked flag in a more serious case when a doctor and an

Wrexham St John's Ambulance pose with a new ambulance outside the County Buildings on Regent Street, 1964.

ambulance was required. They also raised another flag if a veterinary surgeon was required to deal with an injured horse. Harry has forgotten the colour of this particular flag, because he never had to us it. The flags could be seen by officials who scrutinised the course with binoculars during the race. The ambulance could sometimes only get so far, and was unable to reach the victim, and so a stretcher had to be used which could be very difficult over rough terrain, and getting over stiles, etc. and carrying a heavy weight on the return journey. Casualties were taken to the first aid tent, for medical assessment and then hospitalisation if necessary.

Harry Down eventually became a cadet superintendent and continued in this roll after military service in the Second World War. In 1957 he went to Oldham where he was employed as supervisor of the ambulance service there.

St John Ambulance Cadet Band

The St John's Ambulance Cadet Band was formed in 1948, after Mrs F. W. Morris kindly paid for the instruments. An ex-drum-major from the Royal Welch Fusiliers instructed them in band work, and marching. In the 1950s, the drum-major was Richard Evans. They marched every week, in carnivals, fetes, the Mayor's Day and other parades and inspections, and thoroughly enjoyed themselves. Many times their photographs were in the press attending some function or other.

Mr Reg Williams

Reg Williams first started in the St John's Ambulance Brigade in 1938. His father, Mr George Williams, was a founder member of the Wrexham Division, and finally held the post of divisional officer. Reg and his brothers, Alfred, Bob, George and John, all followed in their father's footsteps, becoming members of the St John's Ambulance Brigade.

Reg Williams teaching a group of young St John's Ambulancemen, 1952.

A Saturday afternoon was something to witness at the William's household as each tried to be dressed the smartest, and be out of the door the quickest, to report for duty for either the home football match at Wrexham Racecourse or duty at the various cinemas. Reg, recalls that during his many years service he attended the Bangor Races regularly, also the Llangollen International Eisteddfod and any other major functions held locally. He passed his driving test at the age of 17 years, having been encouraged to do so by senior officials of the St John's Ambulance. He recalled having to attend to some horrendous cases when he was still in his teens and how, as ambulance personnel, they had to answer calls to maternity cases, which always appeared to go into labour at night. In those days they had to pick up the midwife first before the patient. In Wrexham, there was Nurse Mansley, Nurse Forsythe, Nurse Tuite and Nurse Blackwell.

In 1960 Reg was awarded the Priory Vote of Thanks of the Order of St John at Cardiff, and was later awarded the Serving Brother of the Order of St John and, in 1983, Officer Brother of St John. In 1995 he was created a Member of the British Empire (MBE) and presented with the order by HRH Charles, Prince of Wales.

The Williams family of St John's Ambulancemen, father George, and three sons.

Dr Islwyn Jones presents a local ambulance team with a trophy, 1960s.

Left: Members of the Wrexham branch who assisted during the Investiture of the Prince of Wales at Caernarfon, July 1969.

Members of the Wrexham St John's Ambulance Ladies Section in their traditional grey uniform, 1982.

APPENDICES

These lists are by no means definitive but mearly record those names that have been discovered during the research for this book.

1. Wrexham Medical Officers of Health

These are some of the names that I could trace:

1872–81 Dr Joseph Ll. Williams.
1881–1905 Dr Robert William Jonathen Evans.
1906–11 Dr D. Ll. Williams (County MOH)
1911–12 Dr T.W. Jones (District MOH)
1912–16 Dr T. W. Jones (District MOH)
1916–34 Dr Thomas Roberts (District & County MOH)
1920–23 Dr John Lumb (District MOH)
1923–51 Dr T. P .Edwards (District MOH)
1935–48 Dr Arwel Thomas (County MOH)
1950–73 Dr Islwyn Jones (County MOH)
1952–60 Dr Evan Williams (District MOH)
1960–61 Dr Ellis Jones (Dist. MOH)
1961–62 Dr F. Peach (District MOH)
1962–63 Dr D.H. Summers (District MOH)
1963–65 District MOH (position vacant, covered by the County MOH)
1965–74 Dr Alwyn Griffith (MOH)
1974 Local authority re-organisation

2. Wrexham Public Health Inspectors (Sanitary Inspectors)

1875–93 David Higgins
1893–1920 Charles Moore
1820–29 I. A. Stevenson
1930–32 D. B. Davies
1932–37 L. A. Stroud
1944–46 F .G. Davies
1946–74 A. McCartney
1974 Local authority re-organisation

3. Matrons of the Wrexham Hospitals

Wrexham Infirmary

1881 Mrs Townshend
1886 Mrs Noneley
1907 Miss Cragg

The Wrexham & East Denbighshire War Memorial Hospital (approximate dates)

1926 –47/8 Matron Heeley

1947/8–62	Matron Joan Hague
	Asst Matron Miss A. Stanley
	Miss Morgan, Nurse Administrator
	Miss Taylor-Jones, Nurse Administrator
1962/3–82	Matron Dorothy Bridger

Croesnewydd Infirmary/EMS Hospital

early 1930s–1955 (on sick leave 1953–5) Matron Nellie Parry
1930s–1955 (acting Matron 1953–5) Asst Matron Miss Sarah Williams
1953–62 Matron Hammond
1962/3–74 Miss Dorothy Bridger

Maelor General Hospital

1946–55 (on sick leave 1953–5) Matron Nellie Parry
1946–1955 (acting Matron 1953–5) Asst Matron Miss Sarah Williams
1953–62 Matron Hammond
1962/3–74 Miss Dorothy Bridger
1955–71 Asst Matron Miss Dilys Davies (then Matron Llangollen & Chirk)

1974–8 Chief Area Nursing Officer	Miss Dorothy Bridger (based at Preswylfa, Mold).
1974– Nursing Officer Planning	Mr Stanley Wyn Jones (based at Preswylfa, Mold).
1974–8 Principal Nursing Officer	Mrs Kaye Allen (Wrexham Hospitals), retired in 1978.
1980– Chief Area Nursing Officer	Mr Stanley Wyn Jones .
1978–2001 Principal Nursing Officer	Mr Maldwyn Jones (Wrexham Hospitals). His title later changed to Director of Nursing Services.
2001– Executive Nursing Officer	Miss Valerie Doyle.
Asst Director of Nursing Services	Mr Maldwyn Davies.

4. Senior District Nursing and Midwifery Administrators

based at 16, Grosvenor Road, Wrexham

A definitive list of these is unavailable. Some of the incumbents of these posts were:

Miss Chune, Superintendent of District Nurses, Midwives and Health Visitors 1950s–1965.
Miss Eirlys Jones, Assistant Superintendent Supervisor of Community Midwifery Services.
Mrs Laura Warne, 3rd in line. She originally worked as a school nurse during the 1940s & 1950s and was seen quite often in N° 1 Grosvenor Road, where various clinics were held.
Miss Amy Large, Superintendent of District Nurses, Midwives and Health Visitors 1965– 73.
Mrs Ellen Parrish, Supervisor of Midwives 1960–1973.

In 1974 Reorganisation of the Health Service took place and community and hospital nursing staff came under one governing body.

Miss Mary Tagg, District Nursing Officer of Clwyd Nursing, Midwifery and Health Visitor Services, 1973/4 –84.
Miss Joan Gilbert, Divisional Nursing Officer Community Services, alter Director of Community Nursing Services, 1973/4 –86.

In the early 1980s, titles again changed from Divisional Nursing Officers, to Directors of Nursing or Midwifery Services, based at the Maelor Maternity Unit.

Miss Mary Sexton, Divisional Nursing Officer Midwifery, later Director Of Midwifery Services Clwyd South, 1977–88.
Mrs Eleanor Jones, formerly Acting Assistant Director then Director of Midwifery Services Clwyd South 1988–9, transferred to the services of M.A.N.I.N.G. at Glan Clwyd, 1989–91.

Retirement of community midwives, c.1962.

Mrs Barbara Roberts, ex-community midwife, Supervisor/Liaison Officer of Community Midwives Clwyd South, 1978–91 (working under Miss M. Sexton, Director of Midwifery Services Clwyd South.

Mrs Margaret Arkinstall, ex-community midwife, Community & Hospital Midwifery Liaison Officer Clwyd South, 1991–2002.

Miss Menna Williams, Divisional Nursing Officer of Midwifery Services Clwyd North, 1980/1–88, then Director of Midwifery and Gynaecology Services Clwyd (based at the St. Asaph Maternity Hospital) 1988–99.

Mrs Dawn Cooper, Head of Midwifery & Women's Services, 1999. Once more a change in title — Wrexham and District Community Health Services — provided from four health centres and 28 purpose-built, or converted, properties owned by the Area Health Authorities or Trusts, and twelve rented premises. The Community Services covers the following care services: child health, ante-natal, mother-craft, family planning, chiropody, dental care, speech therapy and hearing tests. Health visitors and community nursing staff are mainly based at health centres or clinics. Specialist services are provided by Macmillan nurses,and Marie Curie nurses. A continence advisor is available to provide advice and support to both children and adults. There are also a number of specialist health visitors. A number of para-medics are now working in the community as are speech therapists, audiologists, chiropodists, physiotherapists and a dietician.

4. The names of the Maelor Hospital wards

Male 2 Surgical — renamed Lewis Ward, named after Sir Thomas Lewis (1881–1945), physician to the University College Hospital, London, and director of the Department of Clinical Studies. He pioneered research in electrocardiography, and the physiology of pain, but is remembered chiefly for his brilliant studies in the field of peripheral vascular disease. He was given a knighthood for his work on 'Soldier's Heart' during the First World War.

Male 2 Surgical – became Bright Ward, named after Richard Bright (1789–1858) who was a physician credited with many advances in medicine. Bright's Disease (Nephritis) was named after him.

Male 1 Surgical — became Hunter Ward, named after John Hunter (1728–93). He was elected to St George's Hospital, London where he became a surgeon. He carried out a vast number of experiments in surgery, pathology and allied subjects, and was regarded as the founder of scientific surgery.

Male 1 Medical — became Lister Ward named after Lord Lister (1827–1912). After a brilliant career as a medical student, he went to Edinburgh as a post graduate student to study surgery. He evolved the principles and early practice of antiseptic surgery. By introducing antisepsis to the wards and operating theatres, he made one of the greatest contributions to the advance of surgical techniques, and was regarded as the founder of modern surgery. He was knighted for his valuable work and later given a peerage.

Female 1 Surgical — became Fleming Ward, named after Sir Alexander Fleming (1881–1955) who was a medical student at St Mary's Hospital London. His specialist interest was in bacteriology. He was appointed to the staff of St Mary's and in 1928 became a professor of bacteriology to the University of London. In 1928 that he discovered penicillin, but it was ten years before another group of workers in Oxford realised this, and made possible the miraculous use of the drug in the treatment of infections, introducing the era of antibiotics. He received innumerable honours, including a knighthood and the Nobel Prize.

Female 1 Medical — became Nightingale Ward, named after Florence Nightingale, who carried out great work looking after the wounded soldiers in the Crimean War. She pioneered the nursing profession.

Female 2 Gynaecological — eventually became part of the out-patients department.

5. Names of wards on the Croesnewydd site

Simpson Ward – was named after James Young Simpson 1811–70 whose main aim was to relive the pain of childbirth. Using himself as a guinea pig, he hit on the idea of using chloroform, to relive pain. He encountered a lot of opposition to its use, on religious, moral and pseudo-medical grounds, until it was used by Queen Victoria at the birth of one of her children, which appeared to put the seal of approval on it. He also invented a new type of forceps, used for the delivery of a baby — the Simpson Forceps (low cavity forceps) is still used today and can prevent injury to the soft skull of a premature baby as well as gently deliver the baby when the mother is unable to push the baby out. In 1840 he was a appointed professor of medicine and later professor of antiquities at Edinburgh University.

Blairbell Ward — named after Professor William Blairbell (1871–1936), professor of obstetrics and gynaecology at Liverpool University. He was the founder and first president of the Royal College of of Obstetricians and Gynaecologists and carried our great pioneering work with cancer research.

Lawson Tait Ward — named after Lawson Tait (1845–99) an English surgeon and gynaecologist.

Gilliatt Ward — named after Sir William Gilliatt (1884-1956) an obstetrician to the Royal family and president of the Royal College of Obstetricians and Gynaecologists from 1946–9.

Bonney Ward – named after Victor Bonney (1872–1953) a pioneer of gynaecological surgery.

Alyn Ward — named after the local river.

Ceiriog Ward — named after the local river.

Dee Ward — named after the local river.

Gwenfro Ward — named after the local river which flows through the hospital site.

Acton Ward — named after the local area.

Glyndŵr Ward — named after the local area.

Wynnstay Ward — named after the local area.

Yale Ward — named after the local area.

Samaritan Ward — named after the biblical story of the Good Samaritan.

Lewis Carroll Ward — a paediatric ward named after the author of *Alice in Wonderland.*

Hans Anderson Ward — a paediatric ward named after the author of the fairy tales.

Ward names were also inherited from the War Memorial Hospital Wards

Evington Ward— named after a generous benefactor of the War Memorial Hospital.

Mason Ward — probably named after Alderman Job Mason, Mayor of Wrexham when the War Memorial Hospital was opened in 1926.

Overton Ward — named after William Overton a generous benefactor of the Wrexham Infirmary.

Cunliffe Ward — named after the Cunliffe family of Acton Hall, generous supporters of the Wrexham Infirmary.

Morris Ward — named after a generous benefactor of the War Memorial Hospital.

Pantomime Ward — funds were given by the Walter Roberts Pantomime Company to the ward. A brass plaque was placed behind every endowed bed stating which pantomime the money had come from.

Prince of Wales Ward — named after the Prince of Wales (later King Edward VIII and Duke of Windsor) who laid the foundation stone of the Wrexham & East Denbighshire War Memorial Hospital in 1923.

Pasteur Ward — an isolation ward in the old Maelor Hospital, was named after the famous French scientist Louis Pasteur (1822–95) whose interest in modern biology and biochemistry led to his germ theory, pasteurisation and antiseptic operations.He isolated the rabies virus, and was able to judge the 'lag time' before it induced the disease, this then prompted studies of post infection treatment.

6. Medical Practitioners in Wrexham

This includes some hospital practitioners as well as general practitioners.

1788 – early 1800s

Dr Charles Massie	Surgeon	Yorke Street
Dr David Crewe	Surgeon	Hope Street
Dr Thomas Griffiths	Surgeon	High Street
Dr Prosser	Surgeon	High Street
Dr Joseph Wilkinson	Surgeon	High Street
Dr Richard Ayres	Surgeon	Church Street
Dr Worthington	Surgeon	Bridge Street
Dr Thomas Meredith, M.B.	Surgeon	Mount Street
Dr William Lloyd	Surgeon	High Street
Dr William Taylor	Surgeon	High Street
Dr Hugh Hughes	Surgeon	Hope Street
Dr John Jones	Surgeon	Mount Street House
Dr George Lewis		Bank Street

1884

Dr John Dickenson, FRCS	Surgeon	Crescent House, Beast Market
Dr T. M. Evans	Surgeon	Abbot Street
Dr T. T. Griffiths	Surgeon	Chester Street
Dr George Lewis	Surgeon	Hope Street
Dr J. Kenrick Lewis	Surgeon	Hope Street
Dr William Rowland	Surgeon	Pen y bryn
Dr Joseph Thomas	Surgeon	Chester Street
Dr Edward Williams, MD	Surgeon	Holt Street House
Dr Thomas Eyton Jones, MD, FRCS	Surgeon	Grosvenor Lodge
Dr Richard Williams	Surgeon	Pen y bryn
Dr Drinkwater	Surgeon	Grosvenor Lodge
Dr Augustus Henry Churchill	Surgeon	Pen y bryn
Dr Henry John Barman	Surgeon	King Street

1886

J. Dickenson, FRCS	Surgeon	Horsemarket
E. Davies, MD	Surgeon	27 Regent Street
R. W. J. Evans, MRCPS, LRCS	Surgeon	Bridge Street House
T. Eyton-Jones, MD	Surgeon	Grosvenor Lodge, Regent Street
Alexander Johnston, MB	Surgeon	
Dr J. Jones	Physician	Henblas, Stansty
H. V. Palin, MB	Surgeon	6 Derby Road
Edward Williams	Surgeon	Holt House, Holt Street
Richard Williams, MRCS	Surgeon	
Williams & Evans		3 Regent Street

1912

J. E. H. Davies, MRCS	Surgeon	Grosvenor Road
H. Drinkwater, MB	Surgeon	Grosvenor Road
E. D. Evans, MRCS	Surgeon	Egerton Street
Dr R Evans	Physician	Chapel Street

S. E. Jones	Surgeon	Holt House, Holt Street
E. Moss, BSc, MRCS	Surgeon	Grosvenor Road
H. V. Palin	Surgeon	Horsemarket
F. S. Rowland	Surgeon	9 Bridge Street
Dr T. O. W. Russell	Physician	24 Belle Vue Road
Dr Russell	Physician	Chester Street
J. D. Walker, MB, ChB	Surgeon	Wrexham Infirmary
F. Whitelaw	Surgeon	Grove Park
R. Williams, MRCS	Surgeon	24 Egerton Street
R. G. Williams, MRCS	Surgeon	24 Egerton Street

1951

J. M. S. Spalding	Kumara Lodge, Chester Road
R. S. Brock	Greystones, Chester Road
E. M. Brock	Greystones, Chester Road
M. R. Bull	40 St George's Crescent
Eric A. R. Evans	Chapel Street
D. B. Evans	19 King Street
W. Glyn Evans	Plas Gwilym, 2 Grove Road
A. Wesley Hill	Plas Dinas, Chester Road
W. H. M. Jones	71 Ruabon Road
G. E. Morgan	Bryn Issa House, Bridge Street
W. O'Callaghan	The Chalet, Park Avenue & 40 St George's Crescent
D. Livingstone Pow	15 Holt Street
J. Reid	Pen-y-maes Avenue & 3 Grosvenor Road
S. Stevens	17 Grove Road
Donald Wallice	Leaside, 96 Rhosddu Road & 40 St George's Crescent

7. Early pharmacists

Rowlands

In 1810, Edward Rowland (who had served an apprenticeship with a druggist in Back Chamber Street) established himself as a chemist and druggist at N° 42, High Street, Wrexham, having purchased the business from an apothecary named Powell. When he took over the business he also acquired some of the old records, and the drugs which were said to have been included a jar of 'Dried Woodlice' and a peculiar concoction of 'Vipers in Honey'.

Edward Rowland was born at Llwyn Onn, Abenbury and married Mary Langshaw of Chester, and farmed at Pickhill near Marchwiel, and held a commission in the Denbighshire Yeomanry. In 1826 he died leaving a widow and five children. His sons carried on the business with the help of their mother.

In 1839, the business moved premises to N° 9, High Street, Wrexham, where they installed a new shop front and lived in accommodation above. Edward Rowland's son, William, was Mayor of Wrexham in 1869–70. In time, the family built up the business which became very prosperous, and was eventually handed down to the sons, grandsons, great-grandsons, and great-great-grandsons.

In 1870 the family moved from their accommodation over the shop, and the whole of 9 High Street, was converted to business premises. The shop opened at 6am in the summer months, and 7am in the winter months, and closed at 9pm. Except on Saturdays when they were opened until 11pm. On market days (Saturdays, and Thursdays) the street was very crowded with stalls and the Rowlands were given 2/6 weekly (12.5p) by the stall holder who occupied his side walk.

The Rowlands business gradually increased and establishments were set up in many rural areas:

High Street, Ruabon (1889)
Station Road, Chirk (1911)
High Street, Overton (1921)
High Street, Coedpoeth (1921)
Market Street, Rhosllannerchrugog (1921)
High Street, Pentre Broughton (1922)
Chester Road, Rossett (1924)

Trelawney Square, Flint (1926)
The Square, Llay (1927)
7, Queen Street, Wrexham (1952)
Wheatsheaf Lane, Gwersyllt (1954)
3,&4, Church Street, Welshpool (1956)
14, Lord Street, Wrexham (1959)

The depôt and wholesale distribution was originally located at Mitre Building and Well Place, Wrexham, and later at Dolydd Road, off Croesnewydd Road.

J. F. Edisbury, MPS, 3 High Street, Wrexham.

The name Edisbury goes back a long way in the commercial life of Wrexham. Edisbury had the dispensing business long before the resources of pharmacy had developed and reached the high standard of today. The company's laboratory and dispensing department was probably the most complete in north Wales. Every prescription that was made up was recorded and indexed, so that a ready check could be made if anything was required at any time. Poisons and active ingredients were placed on a check list, each dispenser working under strict guide lines with his work being checked by a colleague and then recorded. Mr. C. G Caldecott, MPS, an extremely well-qualified and experienced pharmacist had control of these departments.